Fossils and the History of Life

Written by Peter Sheldon, with contributions from
Douglas Palmer and Bob Spicer

S193 Course Team

Chair: Peter Sheldon (Earth Sciences)

Authors: Douglas Palmer (Consultant)
Peter Sheldon (Earth Sciences)
Bob Spicer (Earth Sciences)

Critical Reader: Peter Skelton (Earth Sciences)

Course Manager: Isla McTaggart

Science Short Course Programme Director: Elizabeth Whitelegg

Editors: Gerry Bearman, Janice Robertson, Pamela Wardell

Graphic Artist: Sue Dobson

Designer: Jenny Nockles

Picture Researcher: Lydia Eaton

Course Assessor: Professor Euan Clarkson, University of Edinburgh

Illustration on title page Reconstruction of a typical scene in a shallow Silurian sea about 430 million years ago. The Wenlock Limestone was deposited in this setting. See Section 3.4 for further discussion.

The Course Team would like to thank the following: Andrew Smith and Paul Taylor (Natural History Museum), Adrian Lister (University College, London), Colin Scrutton (University of Durham), Alan Thomas (University of Birmingham) and Kevin Page (English Nature) for advice on particular fossil groups; Rod Long of the Sedgwick Museum, Cambridge and Paul Smith of the Lapworth Museum, Birmingham for the loan of fossil specimens; Jirí Kvacek of the National Museum of the Czech Republic, Prague for assistance with photographing fossil plants; Andrew Lloyd and John Taylor (Earth Sciences) for help with electronic images; and Dave Williams and the staff of GEOU for making the fossil replicas.

The Open University, Walton Hall, Milton Keynes, MK7 6AA, United Kingdom

First published 2001. Reprinted 2001

Edited, designed and typeset by The Open University

Printed in the United Kingdom at the University Press, Cambridge.

ISBN 0 7492 3569 1

This publication forms part of an Open University course S193 *Fossils and the History of Life*. Details of this and other Open University courses can be obtained from the Call Centre, PO Box 724, The Open University, Milton Keynes MK7 6ZS, United Kingdom: tel. +44 (0)1908 653231, e-mail ces-gen@open.ac.uk

Alternatively, you may visit the Open University website at http://www.open.ac.uk where you can learn more about the wide range of courses and packs offered at all levels by the Open University.

To purchase this publication or other components of Open University courses, contact Open University Worldwide Ltd, The Berrill Building, Walton Hall, Milton Keynes MK7 6AA, United Kingdom: tel. +44 (0)1908 858785; fax +44 (0)1908 858787; e-mail ouwenq@open.ac.uk; website http://www.ouw.co.uk

S193i1.2

Contents

Understanding fossils

1

1.1 Introduction

Fossils have an immediate and intrinsic appeal for many people. Apart from being intriguing, often beautiful objects in their own right, they provide a link to mysterious worlds we can never experience — worlds that existed often millions of years ago, long before our own species appeared on the scene.

Several early thinkers, such as the Greek historian Herodotus, deduced as early as the 5th century BC that shells now found on mountains were the remains of ancient sea creatures. Herodotus went on to reason that the rocks containing these fossils must have been formed under the sea. However, along with many other perceptive ideas of the ancient Greeks, this theory became lost for about 2000 years. By the time the ideas of evolution by natural selection were being debated in the nineteenth century, fossils were seen as providing the only direct evidence of life's evolution through time that we have. This, above all, is perhaps their most significant legacy; without fossils we would not know, for example, that dinosaurs ever existed or when trees first appeared.

A fossil is simply any evidence of ancient life, naturally preserved within the materials that make up the Earth. Usually, such evidence is found within a sedimentary rock — once loose sediment such as mud, silt, sand or even volcanic ash, but other possibilities for entombment include natural tars and resins, or even ice. There is no strict dividing line in terms of age between recent organic remains and fossils. As a rough guide, most palaeontologists (people who study fossils) would probably consider any evidence of life over about 10 000 years old to be a fossil; the question of definition is not usually an issue, however, as most fossils are millions of years old.

At the start of the course, we'll find out what determines whether an organism has any chance of becoming part of the fossil record, and what processes are involved in fossil preservation. We will also see how fossils are named, how they can be interpreted as once-living organisms, and how they can be dated. We finish Section 1 by considering aspects of reconstructing the past, and some points about evolution and its key process of natural selection.

Then, starting with Section 2, we embark on an overview of the history of life. With the help of the *Atlas of the Prehistoric World* (abbreviated hereafter to the *Atlas*, or *Atlas G* for the glossary), we'll find out just how long after life's origin it took for complex organisms to emerge, and how, in a sudden burst of evolution, a wide range of animals appeared around 545 million years ago. We shall get glimpses of early life in the sea, its eventual expansion onto land, and its proliferation into the spectacular diversity we see today. Sections 3, 4 and 5 cover in chronological order the three great eras making up the last 545 million years. As we proceed, activities with the fossil replicas will enable you to develop the skills of making and recording observations of three-dimensional specimens, and of interpreting aspects of the biology and environment of ancient organisms.

Somehow, life has persisted on Earth for nearly 4 billion years, but it's been far from plain sailing: extinction has been the natural fate of the vast majority of species that have ever lived. As we will see, from time to time mass extinctions have wiped clean much of life's slate, leaving survivors blessed perhaps as much by good luck as good genes.

The Earth is an intensely dynamic planet. Unlike our nearest neighbour, the Moon, the surface of our world is not only teeming with life, but reveals its ceaseless activity in countless other ways: rough seas, surging tides, thunderstorms, waterfalls, avalanches, landslides, volcanoes and earthquakes. Nowhere on Earth is immune from change, and on a geological time-scale some changes can be hard to believe, based on the experience of a single human lifetime. The highest rocks in the world, at the top of Everest, were once under the sea; the Earth's driest deserts will be covered by ocean waters at some time in the future, and one day, for instance, lava will probably spew out over what in its present arrangement of land and sea we call the British Isles. Changing environments such as these have provided the context in which life on Earth has evolved.

By looking at processes operating on the Earth's surface today and the products of those processes, we can learn to recognize their ancient equivalents in the rock record. For the pioneers of geology in the eighteenth and nineteenth centuries, the principle that 'the present is a key to the past' became the best approach to understanding the features of the Earth, and it remains the quickest way to unravel really ancient history.

In recent decades, however, many geologists have returned to a view commonly held in the 19th century, that certain events in the distant past (such as massive volcanic eruptions) have far exceeded anything known in recorded human history, and that these events have had a disproportionate influence on the evolution of life.

Were it not for ancient life we would have no fossil fuels — coal, oil and natural gas, all of which originate from organisms. When geologists are searching in rocks for these vital energy resources they routinely use fossils to match up rocks of the same age from place to place. Recently, as we begin to grapple with the environmental consequences of burning fossil fuels, especially climate change, 'the past is the key to the future' has become an important concept. In order to help predict the future, and perhaps avoid disasters, we need to know about past climatic conditions, how rapidly they have changed, and so on. Because of their ability to record environmental change, fossils have a major part to play in this too.

The story of life and environments through time is mostly preserved in strata — sedimentary layers. These are the diaries of Earth history, containing as they do a record laid down one layer upon another, like successive pages in a journal. But many such pages are missing from the diary, and even where the pages survive, there may be little or nothing written on them, all evidence of life having long vanished. So, deciphering the history of Earth and its life is a major piece of detective work — a multidisciplinary endeavour that, more than any other science, constantly involves changing scales of time and space. For example, atoms build into minerals, minerals into rocks, and rocks into continents — which themselves, like life, are continually changing. Life is made up of atoms, cells, tissues, organs, individuals, populations, species and ultimately the entire biosphere, and the organic and inorganic worlds interact with each other over all these scales in highly complex ways.

Uncertainties exist in all branches of science, and there are obvious uncertainties when trying to reconstruct life and events that happened millions of years ago. Many aspects are not amenable to controlled experiments, there can be huge numbers of variables, and observations may be incomplete. It is in the nature of science that any interpretation is, in theory, capable of being overturned in the light of new discoveries. Bear this in mind as you study the course.

1.2 Getting into the fossil record

Evidence of ancient life can take several different forms. A fossil can be part of the body of an ancient organism, such as the bones of a fish (Figure 1.1a), or the signs of an organism's activities, such as the footprints left by a dinosaur in wet sediment, now a hard rock (Figure 1.1b). In some rocks the only evidence of life may be chemicals that we know can only have been produced by life processes — so-called 'chemical fossils'. **Chemical fossils** can only be detected with specialist analytical equipment and are considered only rarely in this course (Section 2). Overall, they are much less important than body fossils and trace fossils.

Note: in this course we will often use the abbreviation Ma for 'million years'. (M is the scientific abbreviation for a million, and a is short for *annus*, Latin for year.)

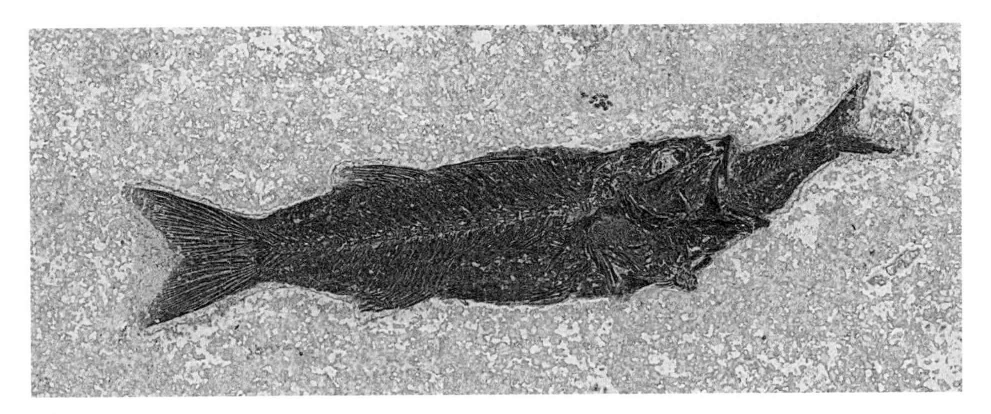

(a)

(b)

Figure 1.1 (a) Fossil fishes that were living about 50 Ma ago, revealing a clear case of greed. The larger fish overestimated its appetite and choked to death trying to swallow the smaller fish. (b) Trace fossils: the tracks of five dinosaurs that walked across what is now part of Colorado, USA about 150 Ma ago. The lateral spacing and parallel direction of the tracks suggest that these dinosaurs moved around in social groups.

Body fossils preserve something of the *bodily remains* of animals or plants, such as shells, bones and leaves, or their impression in the enclosing sediment. It does not matter whether or not the parts of the body have been altered in chemical composition and physical structure. **Trace fossils** preserve evidence of the *activity* of animals, such as their tracks, trails, burrows, or borings. Trace fossils are often the only evidence we have of extinct organisms whose bodies lacked any hard parts (like many types of worm). Even if the organism that made a particular trace fossil had hard parts, the culprit is very rarely found at the scene — at the end of the track or trail. Trace fossils do, however, have one major advantage over body fossils. Unlike body fossils, in which the body may have been transported after death a long way away from where the original organism lived (by currents, for example), most trace fossils are direct, *in situ* evidence of the environment at the time and place the organism was making its living.

- Which of the following fossils are body fossils, and which are trace fossils? (a) the eggs of a dinosaur (*Atlas*, p.109); (b) bite marks of the greedy fish on the smaller fish in Figure 1.1a; (c) the moulted shell of a lobster; (d) the footprint of one of our hominid ancestors (*Atlas*, p.145); (e) the cave painting of a mammoth by early humans who lived in the Ice Age (*Atlas*, p.155); (f) the hair of a woolly mammoth. Note that at this stage there is no need to read the pages associated with the illustrations in the *Atlas*; we'll indicate later when you should read them.

- (a), (c) and (f) are body fossils. The shell moulted by the lobster (c) was part of its body, so it is a body fossil. Any marks made in the sediment as it struggled to shed its shell would be trace fossils. (b), (d) and (e) are trace fossils. The bite marks of the greedy fish are a trace fossil, but the rest of the bitten fish is a body fossil. Footprints and the cave painting of a mammoth are certainly evidence of activity (rather than part of a body), so they are trace fossils.

Although the fossil record as a whole represents a very small proportion of past life, some types of organism leave a pretty good record, with abundant fossils. An organism's **preservation potential** — the chance that it has of getting into the fossil record — varies a great deal according to a range of factors, such as whether its body has any durable parts, where it lives, whether it becomes buried in sediment and whether that sediment subsequently becomes part of the rock record.

Look at Figure 1.2, which shows a scene on the coast of South Wales near St David's. Somewhere in the scene are the following organisms: (a) a rabbit in the fields above the cliffs; (b) a flower growing in the foreground; (c) a thick-shelled limpet attached to the rocks along the shoreline; (d) a cockle burrowing in sand out at sea. Think for a moment about the chances that each one has of getting preserved in the fossil record.

(a) A rabbit certainly has hard, potentially fossilizable bones and highly resistant teeth, but if it dies a natural death its remains will probably be chewed and dispersed by scavengers, and exposed to the elements. Any remaining soft tissues will soon be eaten and decomposed by small organisms, especially bacteria. The bones and teeth may be worn down by movement in a stream, and possibly covered over by sediment. Any burial is likely to be very short lived, however, and the remains may soon be exhumed by erosion during the next storm and, eventually, after many such episodes, be completely weathered away.

(b) The flowers growing in the foreground do not generally have durable parts, and their petals, stem, roots, etc. will rot away quickly in this exposed environment. One part of them, however, has a high preservation potential — their pollen.

Figure 1.2 A coastal scene near St David's, South Wales. See text.

Some of the pollen grains are likely to be blown far out to sea and settle into the sediment accumulating there. Pollen grains (Figure 1.3) are abundant and exceedingly resistant to decay, and fossil pollen grains can be released by dissolving sedimentary rocks in hydrofluoric acid — the powerful acid capable of etching glass. The pollen grains survive this treatment, and can be studied under a microscope. Changes in types of pollen in the fossil record can indicate changing climates, such as a shift from wet to dry conditions, or from warm to cold.

(c) The shell of a limpet, being hard and relatively thick, protects the animal from attack by the sea and from predators. This thick shell might at first seem to give the organism a good chance of fossilization. However, once dead, the shell would soon fall off the rock. It would then usually be broken up by waves and strong currents along the rocky shoreline.

(d) A cockle burrowing in sand out at sea has the highest preservation potential of these four organisms. It has a hard shell, and it is already living within sediment and making potential trace fossils (its shallow burrows).

The land tends to be a site of net erosion, and the sediment that starts off in rivers and lakes mostly ends up in the sea, especially the shallow seas on the edges of continents. This opportunity for long-term burial is one of the main reasons why animals from shallow marine environments dominate the fossil record, and why fossils of land-based organisms are scarce.

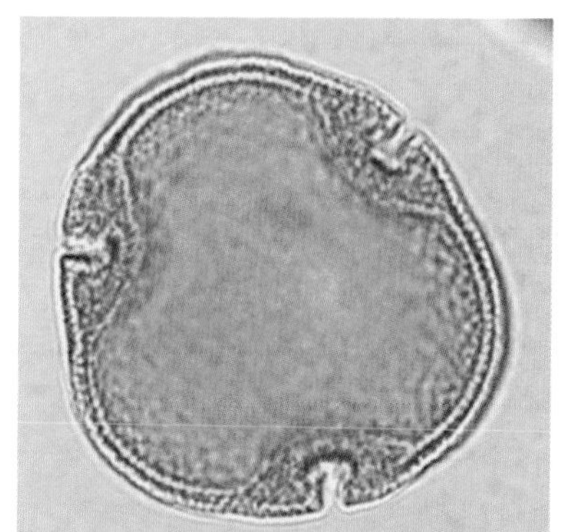

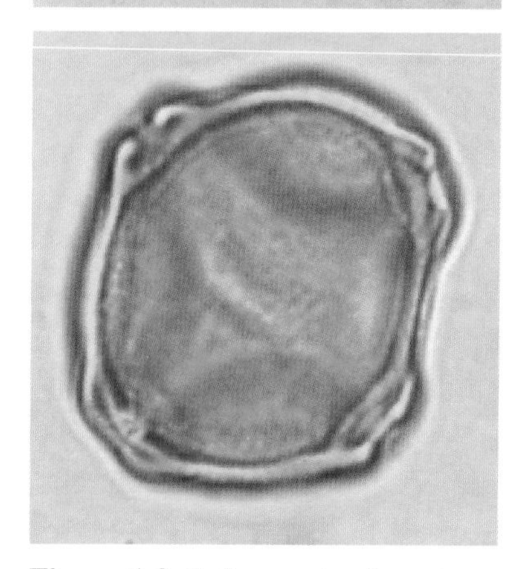

Figure 1.3 Pollen grains from two types of tree: (a) lime (*Tilia*) (0.040 mm); (b) alder (*Alnus*) (0.035 mm). These grains are only about 5000 years old, but much older ones are often just as well preserved.

Question 1.1 Consider the following individual organisms, and assess their likely long-term preservation potential as fossils, taking into account the structure of their bodies and the environment they live in: (a) a garden slug; (b) a garden snail; (c) a whale; (d) a jellyfish. ◀

So, the preservation potential of an *individual organism* depends mainly on:

(a) its *morphology* (i.e. structure and composition), particularly the presence or absence of robust hard parts;

(b) where it lives and the circumstances of its death, and especially whether or not it is buried in a marine environment where sediments tend to accumulate; and

(c) whether or not its activities are likely to produce trace fossils.

Box 1.1, *Is there such a thing as perfect preservation?*, discusses just how good fossil preservation can be.

- The preservation potential of any particular *species*, rather than just an individual member of it, is affected by two other crucial factors. What are they?

- The number of individuals in the species and its geographic distribution.

The more abundant the species is, the higher its preservation potential. Species with a small average size (like the chambered microscopic organisms called forams — or, more long-windedly, foraminiferans — shown in the *Atlas*, p.153) tend to be much more abundant than very large species (e.g. the marine lizard shown in the *Atlas*, p.103, which grew up to 10 m long), and so are more likely to be preserved somewhere in the fossil record (even if they are much less conspicuous). As far as numbers of individuals are concerned, the majority of fossils are, in fact, microscopic. In addition, a wide geographical distribution also increases the chances of a species being found in the fossil record.

When an organism dies it is usually destroyed by scavengers and various decay processes, and its component parts are recycled. The chemical constituents of the dead are made available for the living. Under certain circumstances, however, this recycling is at least partially prevented and the organism ends up as a fossil. Different components of animals and plants have different resistances to decay. For example, in plants, the material called lignin that makes up wood is more resistant than the cellulose that makes up the walls of most other plant cells. Plant fossils (such as roots, stems and leaves) often occur as compressed organic remains made only of carbon, the largely decayed tissues having collapsed under the weight of overlying sediment. To preserve evidence of animal cells (which do not have a cellulose wall around them) requires rapid exclusion of air and immersion in fluids that can penetrate and seal the cells with rapidly forming minerals. Alternatively, the cells need to be entombed in organic compounds with natural anti-bacterial properties, such as tars or resins (see Box 1.1), though on a geological time-scale these materials tend to be relatively short lived.

Some surprising processes can favour fossilization. Fire, usually an agent of destruction, is actually an important contributor to the fossilization of plants. Forests can catch fire from lightning strikes or volcanic eruptions, but burning may be incomplete, and charred remains of plants may survive as charcoal. The plants' organic material, reduced to elemental carbon, is unpalatable to all consumers (which might otherwise eat it) and to decay-inducing organisms such as bacteria. Thus some of the original plant material becomes inert and, if buried, can survive unchanged over millions of years, preserving exquisite details of cells and tissues (Figure 1.5).

Question 1.2 Consider the following species and, ignoring any effects of human predation, assess their *overall* preservation potential in the fossil record as a species: (a) the blue whale (population a few thousand individuals); (b) the garden earthworm; (c) an early species of our genus, *Homo*, with a very small total population that lived in the tropics a million years ago; (d) a common species of oyster with a thick shell. ◀

Box 1.1 Is there such a thing as perfect preservation?

Given all the factors that act *against* preservation, it is surprising that some extremely delicate forms of life have found their way into the fossil record; examples range from the cells lining the stomach of a 100 Ma old fish, and the soft tissues of its last meal, to the butterfly in Figure 1.4.

Consider for a moment what must have occurred for this particular butterfly to have been preserved so well.

For a start, it had to be sealed off quickly from various agents of destruction.

- What general kinds of agents of destruction can you think of that the butterfly must have been protected from?

- The butterfly must have been sealed off from (a) some of the *biological* agents of destruction, such as scavengers that might have eaten it; (b) *physical* agents of destruction such as strong winds or water currents that would have broken up its fragile body; (c) *chemical* agents of destruction such as oxygen (which enhances decomposition), or solutions that might have dissolved away all its organic remains.

In fact, the butterfly came to rest on very fine-grained sediment at the bottom of a stagnant (oxygen-poor), current-free lake, and was gently covered over by a rain of further fine sediment. The fact that the sediment is very fine-grained indicates weak or absent currents, which would be unlikely to damage the butterfly.

- Can you suggest another reason why *fine*-grained sediment is significant for the preservation of this butterfly?

- Small grains favour the preservation of delicate structures and fine details, because the grains can fit closely around them.

Imagine that the butterfly had instead come to rest on a bed of gravel, and been covered over by more gravel. Apart from the fact that currents strong enough to transport gravel would break up the butterfly, the large gravel particles could not mould closely around its delicate structures, and it would soon be obliterated. The durability and preservation quality of any potential fossil thus decreases as the grain size of the enclosing sediment *increases*.

Rapid, permanent burial by fine sediment in oxygen-poor environments is one of the most favourable situations for fossil preservation. This is what has happened to the exquisitely preserved fossils of Messel in Germany, such as the snake and early horse on pages 132–133 of the *Atlas*. But although extremely fine details can be fossilized in the right physical and chemical conditions, there is strictly no such thing as the *perfect* preservation of an entire organism, though this phrase is often loosely used.

Studies of fossil insects and other organisms preserved in amber (a sticky resin produced by certain trees; *Atlas*, p.139) have failed to confirm initial reports that DNA (genetic material; *Atlas G*, p.207) had survived; the genetic material analysed has been re-interpreted as modern contamination. It is virtually certain that *no* DNA can have survived from organisms alive millions of years ago, such as Jurassic dinosaurs. DNA has been recovered from some fossils less than 100 000 years old, such as the frozen flesh of mammoths (including the baby mammoth shown in the *Atlas*, p.154), but the DNA is degraded into short fragments.

Figure 1.4 A butterfly that was flapping its wings about 25 Ma ago, in what is now Colorado, USA.

Figure 1.5 Fossil charcoal from a tree about 300 Ma old showing several cell walls. Such exquisitely preserved detail is common in fossil charcoal. Field of view in this scanning electron microscope photo is 0.3 mm.

Hard biological materials such as bones, shells and wood often contain tiny pores (open spaces). When hard parts are lying buried in sediment, any such pores tend to be filled up with minerals that crystallize out from the water seeping through the sediment. If the original spaces in a porous material are impregnated with extra minerals in this way, the material is said to be **permineralized**.

The growth of new minerals at the expense of any original biological material (such as the cell walls of bone or wood) is called **replacement**. The minerals most commonly involved in permineralization and replacement include: quartz (a form of silica, silicon dioxide, SiO_2; this is called silicification; calcite (calcium carbonate, $CaCO_3$); and iron pyrites or 'fool's gold' (iron sulphide, FeS_2). (Don't worry if you're not familiar with the symbols for chemical elements; the chemical formulae of the minerals are simply included here for reference.) Many of the most spectacularly preserved soft tissues in the fossil record, such as the tiny embryo shown in the *Atlas*, p.57, have been replaced by phosphatic minerals, usually calcium phosphate; experiments on decaying modern organisms suggest that the replacement process in such fossils has occurred in a matter of minutes or hours. Both the filling up of pores (permineralization) and the replacement of biological materials may occur in a single fossil. Neither of these processes, which together are called **petrifaction** — 'turning into stone' — *has* to occur for something to be called a fossil; sometimes the fossil can still be composed of the original, barely altered shell or bone.

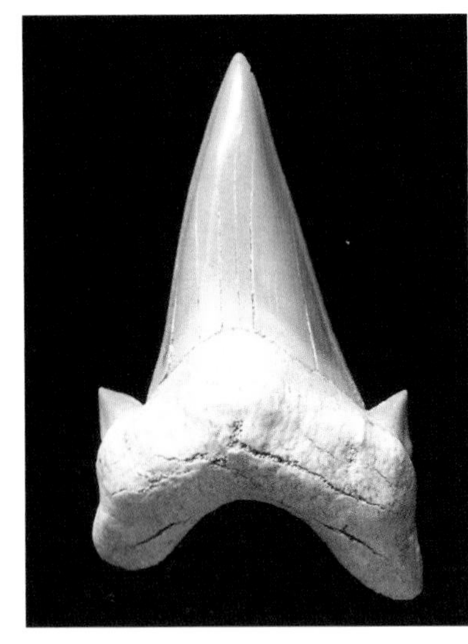

Figure 1.6 A fossil shark's tooth about 6 cm long.

- Sharks have exceptionally durable, though porous, teeth (Figure 1.6). Suppose that there are two shark teeth on a table, each of the same size, shape and colour. One is a fossil and the other isn't. How might you expect to tell the two apart, and why?

- Pick them both up. The fossil is likely to feel heavier. Its density will probably have been increased by additional minerals that have filled up the pore spaces in the tooth whilst it was within the sediment or sedimentary rock.

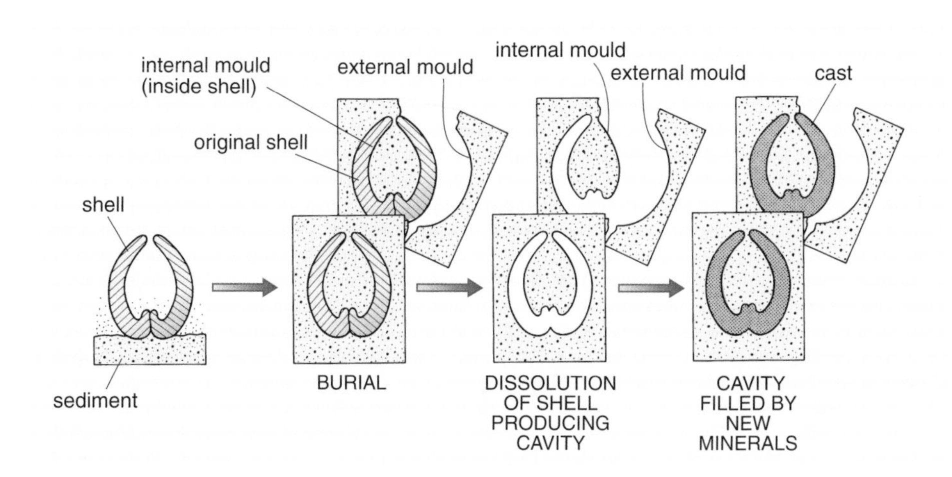

Figure 1.7 Diagram to show the difference between an internal and external mould, and the cast of a fossil shell. See text for further explanation.

Figure 1.8 Internal and external moulds of some snails preserved in sandstone from the Silurian Period. The shells have been dissolved away by percolating acidic water. Some internal moulds have fallen out since the rock was split. Field of view 7.5 cm.

Look at Figure 1.7, which, using a shell as an example, illustrates some terms that are very useful when describing some types of preservation commonly found in fossils. The surface of the sedimentary rock lying against the inside or outside of the shell is called a **mould**, i.e. the impression of the shell's surfaces on the adjacent rock. Usually both internal and external moulds are formed, on the inside and outside of the shell, respectively. Depending on how the rock breaks in the vicinity of a fossil shell, the shell material itself may have to be removed to see the internal mould within or the external mould outside. If at some stage the shell is completely dissolved away (as can occur when percolating groundwater passing through a rock such as sandstone has become acidic), a space is then left between the internal mould and the external mould (Figures 1.7, 1.8). New minerals may then fill up this space, forming a crude **cast** of the shell, which lacks details of the original structure. In general, casts are rarer than moulds. So, a single fossil may show several modes of preservation; most fossil shells, for example, show some degree of replacement or permineralization, and the shells are normally associated with their internal and external moulds in the adjacent rock.

Fossils are much more commonly found than many people realize; they're not just common in textbooks and museums. Many are simply passed by, unrecognized in building stones or underfoot along a rocky beach. Sometimes, however, one can be deceived into thinking an object is a fossil when it is not. Such **pseudofossils** are misleading structures produced by inorganic processes that by chance look as if they are evidence of ancient life. The plant-like pattern in Figure 1.9 is not a fossil at all: it is where crystals of manganese oxide have come out of solution from water passing through cracks in the rock. The crystals have grown on the surface of the limestone in such a way that they look rather like a fern. A similar pattern of ice crystals can sometimes be seen on windows in winter.

Figure 1.9 A pseudofossil, about 7 cm long. See text for explanation.

There are many natural processes that, in the long term, may destroy fossils completely or make them inaccessible to us. Fossil-bearing rocks may be eroded away at the Earth's surface, or buried deep below it. The older a sedimentary rock is, the greater the chance that it has been subjected to high pressures and high temperatures, such as those induced during the collision of continents — and the greater the chance that any fossils originally present have been destroyed. When a rock is squeezed and heated, new minerals are usually formed as the chemical elements in the rock rearrange themselves into more stable arrangements (a process called metamorphism). Most metamorphosed sedimentary rocks therefore lack any evidence of fossils they might once have contained, though sometimes one can see ghostly outlines of organic shapes in marble (once limestone) and slate (once mudstone).

The way that a fossil is preserved clearly determines the amount of biological information it carries to us from the time it was alive. As you study the *Atlas* you will discover that the amount of such information can indeed be remarkable.

Now read the *Atlas*, pp.188–189, which discuss various aspects of fossil preservation.

1.3 The classification and naming of fossils

Before we go further, we need to know a little more about how both living and fossil organisms are classified and named. Think for a moment about the amazing diversity of large organisms familiar to you. It is quite easy to group them simply into animals, plants and fungi. These are three of the major groupings, or **kingdoms**, into which life can be classified. (Other kingdoms can be detected among single-celled organisms, though we need not consider them here.) Almost all plants make their own food by photosynthesis, using energy from the Sun, while all fungi and animals cannot make their own food and are dependent on obtaining food from their external environment. Most animals have the ability to move in search of food, while fungi and plants do not.

It has long been realized that, within the kingdoms, organisms naturally fall into broad groups, each of which is characterized by a distinct arrangement of the body, the **bodyplan**, which is fundamentally different from that of other such groups. Such a group is termed a **phylum** (plural: **phyla**; pronounced 'file-um' and 'file-ah', respectively). For example, humans belong to the Phylum Chordata. There are about 30 animal phyla living today. Experts do not agree on the precise number of phyla, however, mainly because of difficulties concerning whether one regards a particular bodyplan as fundamentally different from other bodyplans or less than fundamentally different.

Within each phylum there are subgroups called **classes**. Each class has its own characteristic modification of the basic phylum bodyplan. There are, for example, five vertebrate classes living today: fish, amphibians, reptiles, birds and mammals, each recognized by their distinctive **morphology**, i.e. their form and structure. Within classes, a nested series of smaller subgroups may be recognized until the level of single **species** — the natural basic unit of classification — is reached. From the class downwards, these groups are **order**, **family**, **genus** (plural: genera; pronounced 'jean-us' or 'jen-us', and 'jen-er-ah', respectively), and **species**. Various intermediate levels are denoted by such prefixes as 'sub-', as in 'subclass' or 'suborder'.

Look at Table 1.1, which shows the classification of the domestic cat. The Felidae is one of eight families within the order Carnivora; *Felis* is one of four genera within the family Felidae; *Felis catus* is one of 31 species within the genus *Felis*. *Felis silvestris*, the wild cat, is another species of *Felis*.

Table 1.1 The taxonomic hierarchy, showing the classification of the domestic cat.

Taxonomic category	Taxon	Contents of taxon
Kingdom	Animalia	all animals
Phylum	Chordata	all vertebrates plus some minor groups
Class	Mammalia	all mammals
Order	Carnivora	all dogs, cats, badgers, seals, etc.
Family	Felidae	all the cat family (lions, tigers, lynx, etc.)
Genus	*Felis*	all wild and domestic cats
Species	*catus*	the domestic cat

The groupings, generally known as **taxa** (singular: taxon), thus form a nested series, or '**taxonomic hierarchy**'. The taxonomic hierarchy should, ideally, reflect evolutionary relationships, with each taxon being a grouping together of all those organisms that share a common ancestor at that level in the hierarchy. The members of successively larger, and therefore more inclusive, groups higher up the hierarchy have fewer and fewer features in common, because they are ever more distantly related to one another, their common ancestor having lived that much longer ago. Interestingly, until recently, all life, past and present, was believed to have evolved from one original common ancestor. It is now thought that for a long time in life's history there was a wide diversity of simple, bacteria-like organisms between which there was extensive transfer of genetic material (as there still is today between bacteria). Only later, when the genes of some, relatively advanced, cells became organized into structures called chromosomes did gene transfer become limited to the extent that a 'branching evolutionary tree' emerged as the predominant pattern. Like branches in a real tree, the branches of such an evolutionary tree (i.e. the lines of descent), once forked, do not merge together again.

The taxonomic hierarchy has many uses, such as providing an efficient means of identifying a specimen. For example, recognizing that a fossil shell is a bivalve means that we can narrow the search to reference books on the Class Bivalvia (to give it its formal name, which, by convention, is always Latinized). We can then try to decide to which order the bivalve belongs, and so on, until the appropriate species description is found. The available information on the species can then be used to determine, say, its likely geological age, or to infer its life habits and hence what the original environment was like. (The rock containing the fossil may also yield independent environmental evidence.)

Formally, the names of all taxa should begin with a capital letter, except for the species name, which *always* begins with a lower-case letter, even when the species has been named after a person. The species name without the genus has no meaning, as some species names apply to more than one genus. The species name is therefore always given together with the genus name, in italics, e.g. the domestic cat is *Felis catus*. This unique two-part combination of genus and species name, called a **binomial**, is immensely useful for scientific communication, being used throughout the world, whatever the language. Our own species is, of course, *Homo sapiens*. Note that the names of genera and species are always printed in *italics*. If this is not possible (e.g. in handwriting), the labels should be underlined. Thus, '*Felis catus*' and

'Felis catus' are equally acceptable. You may notice that the name of a person (or persons) is sometimes given after the binomial name, especially in more formal scientific publications. For example, the common octopus is *Octopus vulgaris* Cuvier, indicating that Cuvier first described this species of the genus *Octopus*. The author's name may appear in brackets, e.g. the lesser or horned octopus is *Eledone cirrhosa* (Lamarck), indicating that the species was first described by Lamarck but under a different genus name to its current one. The specimen, or specimens, upon which the original author based his or her description (called 'type specimens') are usually conserved in a museum collection, where they can act as reference material for deciding whether an unidentified organism should be classified as that species or another.

As an example of the use of these conventions, turn to the reconstruction of an early vertebrate land community at the bottom of pp.82 and 83 in the *Atlas*. The scorpion is labelled *Pulmonoscorpius* in italics, and as this begins with a capital 'P' this must be a genus name; the species name is not given. The amphibian on the far left is labelled *Balanerpeton woodi*. In this case both the genus and species name are given, and the species, though named after the fossil collector, Stan Wood, begins with a small 'w'. The label by the fishes says 'Lungfish', which, as it is not in italics, is not the name of a genus; it is an informal name.

The most fundamental taxonomic category is the species, because, potentially at least, all members of the same species are closely related and can interbreed to produce fertile offspring. By this definition, any two *different* species are said to be 'reproductively isolated', i.e. incapable of interbreeding to produce fertile offspring.

- Why is this criterion inapplicable to fossil organisms?

- Clearly, it is not possible to resurrect a number of similar-looking but long-dead fossil individuals and test whether or not they can interbreed!

The best that palaeontologists can attempt is to make fossil species live up to a definition such as 'Species are morphologically distinct groups within which variation is of the magnitude expected in interbreeding populations, and between which the differences are of the kind and degree expected to result from reproductive isolation in natural populations'. Such a judgement, even if the fossil group has living representatives, is open to subjective influence, and in reality all fossil species are necessarily based on details of their morphology alone. In practice, *living* species also are very often recognized on the basis of possessing very similar physical (and sometimes behavioural) features, rather than a tested ability to interbreed. There are also many taxa, especially among plants, which breed *asexually*, at least for most of the time.

- Apart from the difficulty of trying to decide whether fossil organisms were sufficiently similar to be capable of successful interbreeding, can you think of another problem that palaeontologists often encounter when describing fossil species?

- Fossils often occur as isolated fragments (or moulds in the rock), rather than the whole organism, and it may be difficult to decide whether separate fragments belong to the same species or different species. Also, of course, there is usually no evidence of soft parts, let alone genetic material.

The problem of isolated fragments is especially acute with plant fossils, although it can occur with animal fossils too (as you'll soon see on p.65 of the *Atlas*). Linnaeus, for example, described whole living plants in which all the parts are at some stage attached to one another, so the relationships between the stem, leaves, roots, seeds, pollen grains, etc., are clear. Unfortunately, this is not the case with plant fossils. Throughout their lives, plants shed various organs, either for reproductive purposes (e.g. pollen grains and seeds) or to get rid of waste products, damaged or non-productive parts (e.g. leaves during cold, dark winters or flower parts after pollination). A long-lived tree will produce thousands of seeds, hundreds of thousands of leaves, and millions of pollen grains. All these parts can become separated and subject to decay as they travel by wind or water from the growing site to where they eventually become buried in sediment. As a result, the plant fossil record is not one of individual whole plants, but mostly of isolated fragments, transported away from where they were growing and mixed with parts of other plants, usually belonging to different species.

When a new type of fossil plant fragment is discovered and described in the scientific literature, the binomial system is used as usual, but the name refers only to the isolated fragment, not the whole plant, which may yet be unknown. Eventually, we may find enough attached pieces, originally described as separate fragments, to reconstruct the whole plant. For example, a fossil leaf may be found attached to a twig, which is in turn attached to a flower containing pollen grains. Each part may, however, have originally been given a different genus and species name, and these different names are sometimes retained for separate parts of the same plant. We'll find an example of this in Section 3.8.

Some parts of plants (and animals) are better than others for revealing taxonomic relationships. Consider for a moment a leaf. Its function is to intercept light and photosynthesize as efficiently as possible, despite the various conditions to which it might be exposed. Leaves in the dark understorey of a forest may grow large to intercept maximum light, and despite their large size they can be thin and structurally weak because in their sheltered position wind speeds are low. On the other hand, a leaf at the top of a tree is exposed to high winds, but there is a lot of light. The leaf needs to be strong to survive wind damage, but because light levels are high it can be thick and small instead of thin and large. A leaf, therefore, is genetically programmed to have a variable shape and size, depending on where it is produced on the plant, so leaves can be unreliable indicators of taxonomic relationships. A flower, on the other hand, often acts as an advertisement to pollinators that a reward (e.g. nectar) is available if they visit the flower. As it is so important to attract pollinators, flower morphology is genetically programmed, through evolutionary selection, to remain constant despite local environmental conditions. This is why flower shape rather than leaf shape is used so widely in the classification of flowering plants. Unfortunately, however, as flowers are fragile structures and wither away, they are extremely rare in the fossil record.

There are still uncertainties about the classification of life, though the relatively new methods of cladistics (see *Atlas*, p.187) and molecular genetics (see *Atlas*, *DNA Tree*, p.187) are shedding light on many hitherto puzzling relationships.

Now read the *Atlas*, pp.186–187.

1.4 Interpreting fossils as living organisms

Let's now look at an example of the way in which a knowledge of modern organisms can be used to interpret fossils and give us information about the biology of ancient organisms and the environments they lived in. Although soft parts are rarely preserved in the fossil record, the form of any hard parts is always related to an animal's soft-part anatomy, the way it grows and its mode of life.

As shallow marine **invertebrates** (animals without backbones) dominate the fossil record, let us take two phyla that have hard parts: molluscs and echinoderms, starting with the phylum Mollusca.

Three classes of **molluscs** are abundant and diverse, both today and in the fossil record: bivalves, e.g. cockles and mussels; gastropods, e.g. snails and slugs; and cephalopods (pronounced 'keffallo-pods'), e.g. squid and octopus. Although at first sight these animals might seem completely unrelated to each other, they actually represent variations on the same theme — the bodyplan of the phylum Mollusca. All the various classes of molluscs have diverged in different directions away from a common ancestor.

In most groups of molluscs, the body secretes an external shell (such as that of a snail). **Bivalves**, as their name declares, have a shell in two parts, each part being known as a valve. Except in a few bivalve groups such as oysters, the valves are of equal size and shape, one being the mirror image of the other. From the outside one can see growth lines, such as those visible on the cockle (Figure 1.10a). Each growth line represents the outer edge of the shell at an earlier stage in its life.

On the *inside* of each valve there is evidence that can be used to interpret the bivalve's mode of life. Although the soft parts may have decayed away a long time ago, bivalve shells have distinct areas where muscles for closing the shell were attached. The size, shape and location of these muscle scars reveal aspects of the animal's mode of life. Each valve of the cockle shell (Figure 1.10b) has two muscle scars, between which is a shallow groove. This groove is often visible as a thin shiny band running roughly parallel to the edge of the shell. This shallow groove is where part of the fleshy tissue that secreted the shell was attached.

(a)

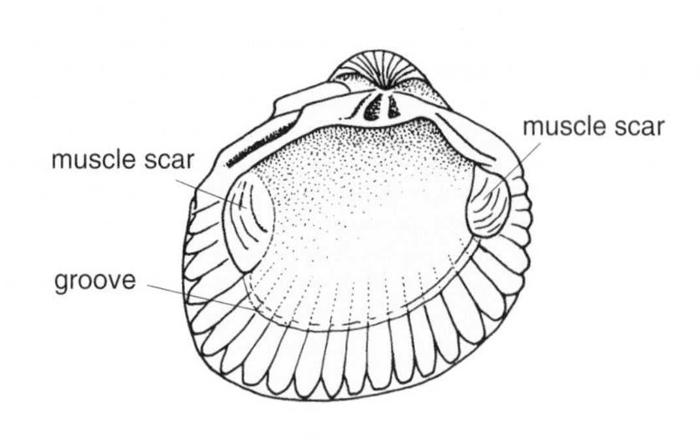

(b)

Figure 1.10 (a) A living cockle, its shell and siphons clearly visible as it lies partly buried in sand. (b) The interior of one valve of the Common Cockle, *Cerastoderma edule*.

In the living cockle, Figure 1.10a, two soft tubular siphons can be seen. One is used for taking in water to structures that absorb oxygen and strain off tiny food particles suspended in the water. The other siphon ejects water containing waste products. Bivalves that live in a deep burrow have long siphons that protrude up above the entrance of the burrow during feeding. A distinct notch in the course of the groove between the muscle scars, if present, indicates where the bivalve could retract its siphons when disturbed (Figure 1.11).

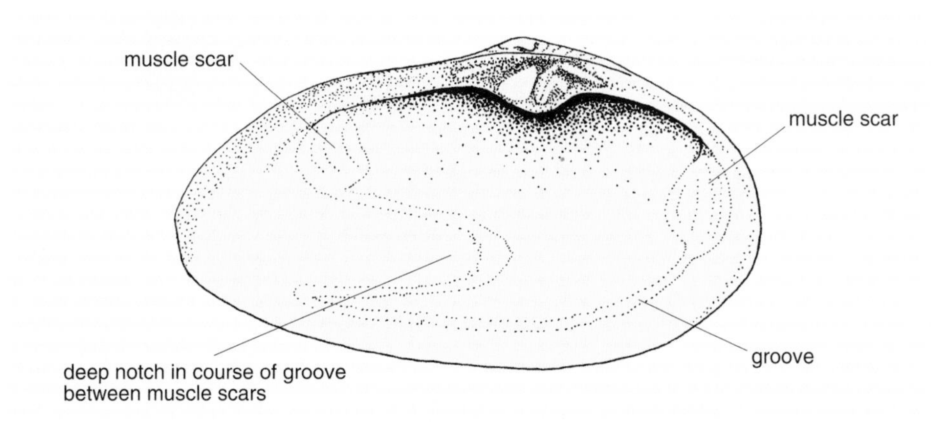

Figure 1.11 The interior of one valve of a modern bivalve (the Common Otter Shell, *Lutraria lutraria*), showing a deeply notched groove between the muscle scars.

- Imagine that you have found an isolated fossil bivalve shell, similar to that in Figure 1.11, and you are trying to interpret its mode of life. You notice it has a deeply notched groove between the muscle scars. What inference would you make from this observation?

- The species was probably a deep burrower.

The deeper the notch, the longer the siphons that were retracted into it. Long siphons are needed if the animal burrows deeply below the sediment surface (as does the species in Figure 1.11). The cockle, by contrast, is a shallow burrower, and so its shell has no such notch (Figure 1.10b).

Echinoderms ('eck-eye-no-derms') are members of another phylum, and so have a fundamentally different bodyplan to that of the molluscs. Among the groups in the exclusively marine phylum Echinodermata are sea urchins (**echinoids**), starfish and crinoids. Echinoderm skeletons are, in most cases, made of many interlocking plates of the mineral calcite (calcium carbonate). In sea urchins, movable spines used for locomotion and defence are attached by muscles to knobs on the plates.

Figure 1.12 (overleaf) shows two views of the edible sea urchin — a living animal covered in spines (Figure 1.12a), and a dead animal with its spines partially missing (Figure 1.12b). The thin tentacles projecting out beyond the calcite spines (Figure 1.12a) are soft, multi-purpose organs called tube feet which the animal uses for feeding, respiration, locomotion and, in some species, constructing burrows. The tube feet project through little pores in the plates of the skeleton. Most of the round sea urchins live by browsing on plant and animal growths covering rocks, whereas oval or heart-shaped ones (with a front and back end) are adapted to burrowing and usually have smaller spines. The mouth is located on the underside.

(a)

pores
plates
spines
knob for spine attachment

(b)

Figure 1.12 (a) A living edible sea urchin, *Echinus esculentus*, with long tube feet extending beyond its spines. (b) Drawing of a dead edible sea urchin with its tube feet decayed. The spines, which usually soon fall off naturally, are omitted from the left side, so that the plates of which the skeleton is made can be shown.

- Which parts of sea urchins mentioned above are most *unlikely* to be found in the fossil record, but which can nevertheless be inferred to have been present because of features of the sea urchin's skeleton?

- The tube feet, which are indicated by pores in the plates, and the muscles that connected the spines to the rest of the skeleton.

Look at the fossil sea urchin in Figure 1.13 and see if you can identify the rows of tiny pores and also the knobs for spine attachment (the spines are missing).

You will soon be applying some of the lessons of this section when interpreting the fossil replicas as living organisms in Activities 3.1, 4.1 and 4.2. Before moving on, try the following question which covers some useful general points.

Question 1.3 Which of the following aspects associated with a fossil organism should make it easier to reconstruct the once-living individual, its activities, and its environment? (a) It has few relatives alive today; (b) it left abundant trace fossils; (c) there are several other fossil groups in the same rock; (d) its hard parts became separated from each other after death; (e) its hard parts are complex, with many detailed structures. ◀

Figure 1.13 The underside of a fossil sea urchin, *Paracidaris smithii*, from the Jurassic Period (diameter 7 cm). The tooth-like plates in the centre, rarely preserved in place like this, are part of its jaw apparatus for scraping up food.

1.5 Geological time and the dating of fossils

In order to study the history of life, we need to be able to place important events in the perspective of geological time. Geologists have subdivided the history of the Earth into time intervals of varying duration. The major boundaries between these time intervals were chosen in the nineteenth century, largely on the basis of major changes in the kinds of fossils found in successive strata. These changes were later recognized as resulting from biological events such as mass extinctions (when many groups of organisms died out), or from mountain-building episodes which left gaps or other features in the sedimentary record that could be recognized over a wide area.

There are two aspects of age: **relative age** and **absolute age**. To illustrate the difference between the two, consider the statement: 'this newspaper is more recent than that one'. It's a clear indication of relative age, but says nothing about the *actual age* of each newspaper, nor the *time difference* between them. The absolute date of a newspaper is the date it was printed, such as 28 March 2001; its absolute age is the time that has elapsed between then and now.

During the early development of geology, only a *relative* time-scale — a sequence of events — was possible. Even nineteenth-century geologists had no reliable way of dating rocks or the age of the Earth, although they generally considered that the Earth was probably a few hundred million years old. Other scientists supported the Scottish physicist Lord Kelvin's calculation that the Earth was only a few tens of millions of years old. Kelvin's calculation was, however, based on the estimated time taken for the Earth to cool by conduction from a wholly molten state to its present temperature (*Atlas*, p.166). He did not take account of the heat energy supplied by radioactivity or its circulation by convection in the Earth's mantle because neither phenomena were known at the time. Consequently, he greatly underestimated the age of the Earth.

Today we can give approximate dates to geological events in millions of years using the methods of **radiometric dating** (*Atlas*, pp.166–167). It is important to realize that all radiometric ages depend on the validity of certain assumptions, and that each age has an associated uncertainty. For example, in the *Atlas*, p.167, the oldest dated mineral is said to have an age of 3962 ± 3 million years; this means that its age could lie anywhere within a span of six million years, i.e. between 3959 and 3965 million years ago.

The study of strata and their relationships in time and space is called **stratigraphy**. Sequences of strata have long been used to establish a generalized geological succession — the **stratigraphic column**. The boundaries between geological periods (and many of the subdivisions within them) have been assigned absolute dates; Figure 1.14 shows this geological time-scale.

The immensely long interval from the origin of the Earth to the start of the Cambrian Period — the **Precambrian** Eon — is sometimes also known as 'the **Cryptozoic**' (derived from Greek words meaning 'hidden life'). The interval from the start of the Cambrian Period to the present day is called the **Phanerozoic** Eon. Phanerozoic is derived from Greek words meaning 'visible life', reflecting the obvious presence of life since the start of this time, when fossils first become abundant. The Phanerozoic Eon is divided into three **eras** — the **Palaeozoic***, **Mesozoic** and **Cenozoic*** Eras (meaning 'ancient life'; 'middle life', and 'recent life', respectively). Each of these eras is divided into a number of **periods** of unequal length (Figure 1.14). The names of periods are variously derived, ranging from the Latin for Wales, 'Cambria'; an area

*Note that Palaeozoic is often spelt in the American way, i.e. Paleozoic, as in the *Atlas*. You will also find alternative spellings for Cenozoic, i.e. Caenozoic or Cainozoic, in some books.

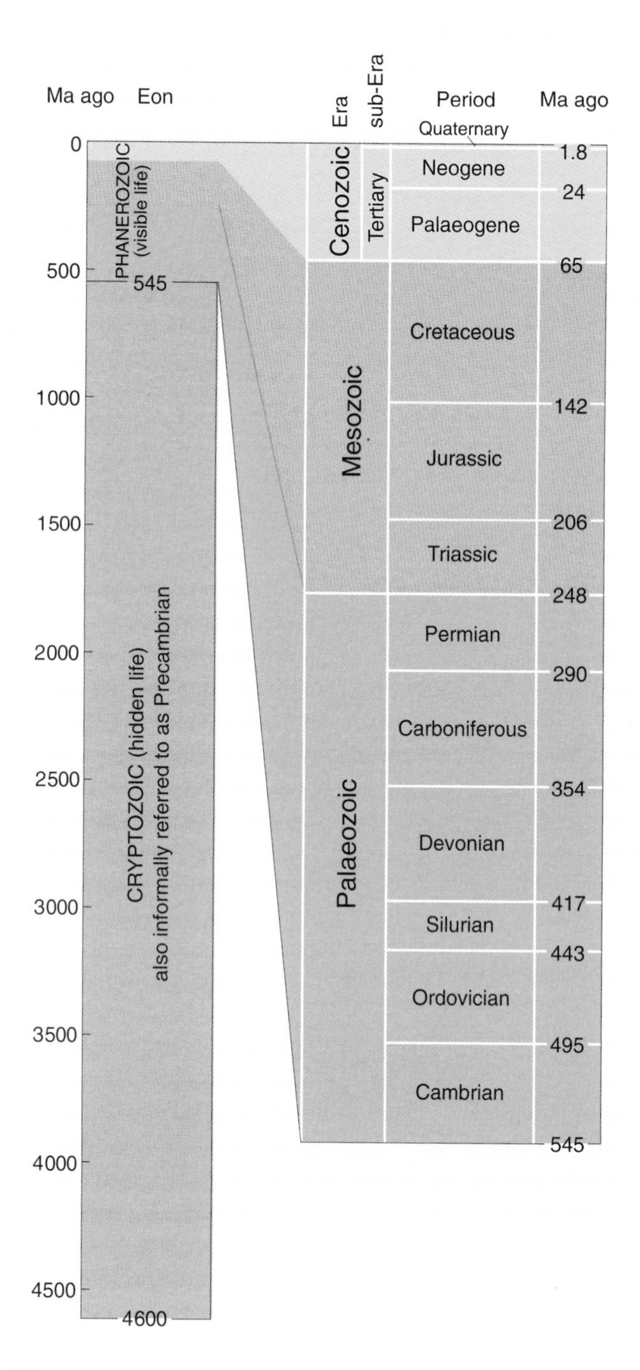

Figure 1.14 The geological time-scale. You will often need to refer to this figure.

of Russia, Perm; to the Latin for chalk, 'creta'. The words 'Eon', 'Era' and 'Period' do not have to be mentioned each time; e.g. it is acceptable, for example, to talk simply of 'life in the Palaeozoic'.

To understand the history of life and ancient environments we need to know what happened at the same time *in different parts of the world*. For example, to get to grips with what occurred when the dinosaurs became extinct, we need to establish whether they all died out at the same time across the globe, or at different times in different areas. The matching up of rocks of the same age from one area to another is called **correlation**.

It was the early nineteenth-century English canal engineer, William Smith (*Atlas*, p.163), who first found he could correlate apparently *dissimilar* strata (e.g. a limestone and a sandstone) because they contained *similar* fossils. Going up though the strata, he observed a succession of different fossils, and proposed that each stage in this succession represented a particular span of geological history. Using this principle (long before any evolutionary explanations were available), he was able to correlate widely separated outcrops of rock by the fossils they contained. This method of using fossils to identify the relative age of strata, and correlate with them, is called **biostratigraphy**. The stratigraphic column is divided into **zones** (or biozones) that are characterized by one or more particular fossil species (called **zone fossils**). The sequence of biozones in the correct order makes up the **biostratigraphic column**. Ideally, to be useful, zone fossils should belong to rapidly evolving groups (with a short time range), have distinctive appearance, be wide ranging geographically (like many free-swimming or floating marine creatures), and be abundant as fossils.

- Considering the criteria required of a good zone fossil, and from your background knowledge of dinosaurs, would you expect dinosaurs to be suitable zone fossils for the Jurassic Period?

- Dinosaurs are very rare as fossils, often found as incomplete remains, and were not marine animals; they would therefore be unsuitable as zone fossils.

Once particular fossils from a rock of unknown age have been identified correctly, it is possible, with access to suitable references, to tell to which particular geological period — or part of it — the rock belongs, providing the succession of fossil species has already been well established. The approximate absolute age (in Ma) can be obtained by referring to an up-to-date geological time-scale, though absolute dates are continuously refined as new data emerge.

There are many other ways of correlating rocks that are independent of the use of fossils, such as recognizing the effects of synchronous changes in global sea level, global temperature (e.g. ice ages) and reversals of the Earth's magnetic field (*Atlas*, p.167), although many of these methods are specific to particular situations or times in Earth's history.

Now read the *Atlas*, pp.162–163 and pp.166–167, and then pp.102–103, 'Discovering Extinction and Deep Time'.

Question 1.4 Test your understanding of some important points in this section by filling in the blank spaces in the following paragraphs with the appropriate words.

The broadest division of Earth history is into two intervals (called eons) of very different length. The earlier .... (1) Eon is a vast amount of time — from the origin of the Earth, ... (2) Ma ago, to .... (3) Ma ago. The later .... (4) Eon extends from .... (5) Ma ago to the present day.

Unless strata have been overturned, which may sometimes happen during mountain building, the deeper down the strata are, the .... (6) they will be. This important principle of relative .... (7) is known as the 'law of .... (8)', first explicitly stated in 1669 by the Dane, Nicolaus Steno. Major time breaks in the stratigraphic record, where strata from a long time interval are missing, occur quite often, and may be widespread across large geographic areas; such breaks are called .... (9). Zone fossils are used to .... (10) (i.e. match up) rocks of the same age in different areas. Ammonites, for example, are used extensively for zoning strata of .... (11) age. Absolute age dates, obtained by radiometric dating, always have .... (12) associated with them, as is shown, for example, by an age expressed as 482 ± 0.5 Ma. ◀

1.6 Reconstructing the past

Read the *Atlas*, pp.190–191 and then pp.182–183. These pages review some of the historical developments en route to our current understanding of ancient life and environments.

With all the accumulated knowledge of today it is easy to forget the huge difficulties that lay in the path of those whose curiosity drove them to make sense of fossils and the rocks containing them. In the eighteenth and nineteenth centuries the most fruitful approach became one of using 'the present as a key to the past', as discussed on p.182 of the *Atlas*. By looking at processes operating on the Earth's surface today, and the products of those processes, geologists learnt to recognize their ancient equivalents in the rock record. For example, geologists could observe eruptions of lava and study the resulting rock (such as basalt) once the lava had cooled. They could then identify *ancient* rocks of a similar nature, and infer that similar volcanic processes were responsible for their formation. But we now know that there are limits to this approach: some events in the distant past (such as huge meteorite impacts and massive volcanic eruptions) have far exceeded anything known in recorded human history. As we'll see shortly, rare events of exceptional magnitude have probably had a disproportionate influence on the history of life, and, furthermore, they will sooner or later recur in the future.

- According to the *Atlas*, the new catastrophism is an important shift in thinking that has occurred in the last decade or so. What is this shift?

- Geologists have come to realize that the impact of rare, natural events can be greater than the cumulative effects of slow and gradual processes between such events. This return to an early nineteenth-century view of the importance of catastrophes is called the new catastrophism (*Atlas*, p.183).

At any one time, the totality of life on Earth has been unique to that moment. Evolution has produced very different forms of life at different times, even if key evolutionary processes (such as natural selection, see Section 1.7) and the basis of the genetic code have essentially remained the same for several billion years. As we saw in Section 1.4, attempts to reconstruct past life largely rely on the ability to relate biological structures found in fossils to those of living organisms.

Question 1.5 What general difficulties often arise when attempting to reconstruct extinct organisms from their fossil record? ◀

Despite these intrinsic problems, reconstructions of prehistoric animals, plants and their environments have continually improved as science has progressed on all fronts. Reconstructions have certainly become a great deal more sophisticated since Richard Owen's first attempt at reconstructing dinosaurs in the mid-nineteenth century, especially in recent years with the availability of computers to generate and manipulate moving images.

- What must always be remembered when viewing such images of extinct creatures, no matter how convincing and realistic they might look?
- They are interpretations that depend entirely on the quality of the fossil data involved, the assumptions made at every stage, and the availability of an appropriate living organism to which the extinct creature can be related (*Atlas*, p.191).

Bear these caveats in mind as you study the reconstructions of ancient life in the *Atlas*.

1.7 Evolution and the fossil record

Evolution is the process of biological change by means of which different types of organisms have inhabited the Earth at different times. A common definition used by biologists is 'any cumulative change in the heritable characteristics of species or populations from generation to generation, or over longer periods'. Darwin used the wonderfully succinct phrase 'descent with modification': descent from an ancestor and modification of biological features with time.

Now read the *Atlas*, pp.192–195.

- Was Charles Darwin the first person to suggest that species were not fixed but could change into other species with time?
- No, a number of earlier people, including Darwin's grandfather, had proposed this at the end of the eighteenth century (*Atlas*, p.192).

It was Charles Darwin and Alfred Wallace who independently first came up with a mechanism for change, and they presented their idea of evolution by **natural selection** jointly in 1858. Darwin's masterpiece *On the Origin of Species* was published a year later in 1859.

Natural selection is such a simple idea in essence that, hearing about it for the first time, the brilliant Victorian zoologist Thomas Huxley said 'How extremely stupid not to have thought of that before!'.

Natural selection can be summarized by two observations and one conclusion:

1 Members of a population always vary, and much of this variation is inherited by the offspring.

2 Populations generally produce more offspring than can possibly survive and breed.

3 In the struggle for existence, the offspring which vary in ways most suited to the environment will survive and propagate, so favourable variation will therefore accumulate in populations by natural selection.

Natural selection is thus the process of differential survival and reproduction of organisms (and their variations) that are best suited to their environment. In any environment space and resources are limited, so there is competition within and between populations. Individuals that possess favourable characteristics, of whatever sort, will tend to compete successfully and leave more descendants than other, less fortunate individuals. In fact, natural selection is inevitable as long as there are three things: a struggle for existence; variation; and inheritance.

Variation is the raw material on which selection acts. As part of his evidence in favour of natural selection as a mechanism for producing new types of organisms, Darwin pointed to the immense amount of potential variation within species revealed by the results of **artificial selection** by plant and animal breeders. Humans, he argued, have, within a very short time (geologically speaking), selectively produced all sorts of different breeds of dogs, cattle, sheep and pigeons, for example. Plant breeders too have repeatedly selected desirable features such as high yield (in crops) and attractive appearance, giving a vast range of new forms, many of which today adorn our gardens or tempt our taste buds on the shelves of supermarkets. Darwin argued that if humans can produce these biological changes in a short time, then natural selection acting on the variation within species over immensely longer periods could lead to far greater changes, and ultimately to the diversity of life we see around us.

The ultimate source of variation is genetic **mutation**, an alteration to the genetic material that can be copied from parent to offspring. This ultimate source of variation — mutation — arises by chance, at random with respect to the needs of present or future circumstances. Natural selection, by contrast, is itself the very opposite of a chance process.

Natural selection has the effect of building up biological complexity gradually, step by step in a cumulative way. It is believed to be the main, but not the only, mechanism of evolution. It's worth pointing out that not all natural selection produces change; it can promote stability, keeping species much the same over long intervals. This type of natural selection occurs when the most common variations are favoured, and individuals with other, perhaps new forms of variation are eliminated.

Darwin argued that the environment varies with time and from place to place. Heritable variations that suit a particular environment will be selected there, and so populations will diverge and become different as each one becomes adapted to its own local conditions. If the differences between diverging populations accumulate to a point where, if brought into contact, the populations are unable to interbreed to produce fertile offspring then, by definition, a new species will have been formed (Section 1.3). This principle of divergence has no limit, so the diversity of life on Earth can be explained by divergent lines of descent from more or less remote common ancestors.

The term **microevolution** is often used today (e.g. *Atlas*, p.193) for any evolutionary changes that occur *within* a species, up to and including the formation of new species. The term **macroevolution** refers to evolutionary changes and evolutionary patterns affecting taxa *above* the level of species, such as the formation of genera, families or phyla.

- Which famous fossil, found in Germany shortly after the publication of *On the Origin of Species*, provided Darwin with a good example of an intermediate form of the kind he predicted should be found in the fossil record between one major animal group and another?

- *Archaeopteryx*, which possessed a convincing mixture of reptilian and bird characteristics (*Atlas*, pp.192–193).

One of the challenges Darwin faced was the criticism that natural selection was flawed because it could not explain the earliest stages of useful structures. How could major novelties get started, such as feathers on the wings of a bird? What good is 2% of a wing for flight? The general answer to such questions, which was much invoked by Darwin, relies on the **principle of preadaptation**. The feature in question once performed a quite different role in ancestors, but was, by good fortune in retrospect, well suited for transformation to serve another function, especially in new circumstances. Alternatively, the preadapted feature may simply have been a consequence of the way the organism was constructed; for example, naturally weak points in some branching corals have become adaptations to break in storms, as an effective means of asexual propagation. In many cases, the intermediate stages of the complex, integrated feature previously had roles that were quite different to their eventual main function. Thus, with the benefit of hindsight, a feature turned out, fortuitously, to have been well suited to perform a radically new function with relatively little change of form.

How might this work with the feathers of early birds such as *Archaeopteryx*? Feathers are actually modified reptile scales. Scaly outgrowths may, by chance, originally have helped in insulation (i.e. controlling heat loss), and even the slightest outgrowths may have conferred an advantage to the individuals possessing them. Alternatively, or additionally to insulation, early feathery outgrowths may have been used for camouflage, for display, or even protection as a tough but light armour, giving individuals with well-developed forms of this variation a better chance of reproduction. Feathers may have served a combination of some or all of these various functions before being co-opted for flight by birds.

- What important aspect was completely missing from Darwin's and Wallace's theories that would have strengthened even further their case for evolution by natural selection?

- An understanding of genetics, especially the underlying mechanisms of inheritance (*Atlas*, p.194).

A number of recent developments are discussed in the *Atlas* (pp.194–195), including the failure to repeat the finding of DNA from insects entombed in amber millions of years old. The supposedly ancient insect DNA is now re-interpreted as modern contamination (as we saw earlier in Section 1.2). As explained on p.194, today the closeness of evolutionary relationships among living organisms can be assessed by comparing details of their genetic code, and the time at which any two organisms last shared a common ancestor (the 'divergence time') can be estimated using the theory of the 'molecular clock'. This is the idea that the molecules which form genes and proteins accumulate small mutational changes in a clock-like, constant rate over geological time. The difference between the form of a molecule in two species is then proportional to the time since the species diverged from a common ancestor.

- What turned out to be wrong about the first ideas of the molecular clock?
- It was found that different molecules changed (mutated) at different rates, and only some molecules kept 'regular time' (*Atlas*, p.194).

Today, evidence from both molecules and the fossil record are used in concert to refine divergence times and establish closeness of evolutionary relationships; sometimes the results are surprising.

- According to recent molecular evidence, to which group are rabbits more closely related, rats or primates?
- Primates (*Atlas*, p.195).

In addition to providing an explanation for evolution (i.e. the mechanism of natural selection), Darwin showed how evolution explained and brought order to the known facts in every field of biology and palaeontology. As one of the greatest biologists of the twentieth century, Theodosius Dobzhansky, wrote in 1937: 'Nothing in biology makes sense except in the light of evolution'. That is not to say no puzzles remain — many do, of course — but evolution provides the overarching process by which we can understand the history of life as revealed by the fossil record. Let's now begin our look at this history of life in Section 2.

1.8 Summary of understanding fossils

A fossil is any evidence of ancient life, naturally preserved within the materials that make up the Earth, usually a sedimentary rock. Body fossils preserve something of the bodily remains of animals or plants. Trace fossils are evidence of the activities of animals, and are a direct indication of the environment at the time and place an organism was living. An organism's preservation potential varies according to many factors, such as whether its body has any durable parts, where it lives and whether it becomes buried in sediment. Rapid, permanent burial by fine sediment in oxygen-poor environments is one of the best situations for fossil preservation. DNA has been recovered from some fossils less than 100 000 years old, but it is degraded into short fragments. Invertebrate animals that lived in shallow seas dominate the fossil record.

Organisms fall naturally into broad groups, called phyla, each of which is characterized by a fundamentally distinct arrangement of the body, the bodyplan. There are about 30 animal phyla living today, though experts disagree on the exact number. Within each phylum, organisms can be classified into a series of increasingly smaller groups, called taxa: class, order, family, genus and species. Each taxon ideally reflects evolutionary relationships, grouping together all those organisms that share a common ancestor at that level. The most fundamental category is the species, because, potentially at least, all members of the same species are closely related and can interbreed to produce fertile offspring. As this criterion cannot be applied to fossil organisms, all fossil species are based on considerations of morphological similarity alone. Today, the closeness of evolutionary relationships among living organisms can also be assessed by comparing details of their genetic code, and evidence from both genes and the fossil record can be used to establish the time at which any two organisms last shared a common ancestor.

A knowledge of modern organisms can be used to interpret the biology of ancient organisms and the environments in which they lived. The form of any hard parts, such as shells and skeletons, is always related to an animal's soft parts, the way it grows and its mode of life. The reconstruction of an extinct organism depends on the quality of the fossil data involved, the assumptions made at every stage, and the availability of an appropriate living organism to which the extinct one can be related.

There are two aspects of a fossil's age: its relative age and absolute age. Approximate absolute ages can be given to rocks and the fossils they contain using the methods of radiometric dating. The immensely long Precambrian interval began with the formation of the Earth 4600 Ma ago and ended 545 Ma ago at the start of the Phanerozoic when fossils first become abundant. The Phanerozoic Eon is divided into the Palaeozoic, Mesozoic and Cenozoic Eras, each of which is made up of a number of periods of unequal length. The boundaries between geological periods often reflect biological events recorded in the fossil record, such as mass extinctions.

The study of strata and their relationships in time and space is called stratigraphy, and the matching up of strata of the same age from one area to another, often done on the basis of finding the same fossil species, is called correlation.

By looking at processes operating on the Earth's surface today and the products of those processes, geologists can recognize the equivalent ancient environments: 'the present is the key to the past'. However, the impact of very infrequent natural events can be greater than the cumulative effects of slow and gradual processes between such events.

Evolution is the process of biological change by which different types of organisms have inhabited the Earth at different times. Natural selection is the key evolutionary process, and involves the differential survival and reproduction of organisms (and their heritable variations) that are best suited to the environment. If the differences between separated populations accumulate to a point where, if brought into contact, the populations are unable to interbreed to produce fertile offspring then, by definition, a new species will have been formed. The principle of preadaptation is used to explain how a major new feature starts to evolve — the feature once performed a quite different function in ancestors that, by good fortune in retrospect, was well suited to perform a radically new function without much change of form.

There are many uncertainties when trying to reconstruct life and events millions of years ago, and it is in the nature of science that any interpretation, is, in theory, capable of being overturned in the light of new discoveries.

2 Early life on Earth

2.1 Life's long fuse to the Cambrian explosion

Read the *Atlas*, pp.50–53.

Today, the consensus view is that life began on Earth at least 3.8 billion years ago and possibly as long as 4 billion years ago. (A billion here, as in science generally, means a thousand million.) The fossil evidence to date shows that there was an immensely long phase of evolution before many groups of organisms with preservable hardparts evolved rather suddenly in the Cambrian 'explosion', around 545 Ma ago (Section 3.1).

Perhaps surprisingly, as little as 100 years ago scientists did not know about life's long 'fuse' prior to the Cambrian explosion, and many considered that life had not begun until Cambrian times. Mapping rocks of North Wales in the 1830s, Adam Sedgwick (*Atlas*, p.201) produced evidence that fossils first appeared in particular strata that he called Cambrian in age (naming them after the Roman name for Wales, Cambria). These rocks were not very fossiliferous but did contain various shelly fossils such as trilobites, which were for some time considered to be among the earliest life forms on Earth. A Cambrian trilobite is shown on p.61 of the *Atlas*.

Geologists like Sedgwick thought that the more ancient *Pre*cambrian rocks were completely devoid of fossils. The first suggestions of Precambrian life were not found until about 1860, in ancient rocks of Canada. However, despite initial excitement, these supposed remains of some kind of single-celled organism were later shown to be of inorganic origin. Indisputable fossil evidence for Precambrian life was not generally accepted until details of the 1.9 billion year old Gunflint microfossils (*Atlas*, p.50) were first published in the 1950s.

At the same time as nineteenth-century geologists were discovering relatively well preserved Precambrian strata that might hold clues to the origin of life, biologists were revealing an astonishing diversity of life on Earth, especially the wealth of microorganisms that live in water. It soon became evident that there must have been a number of important evolutionary stages as life became more complex in its organization. The question became: would any such stages be preserved within the Precambrian record?

Let's consider what some of these stages might be by briefly comparing the basic biology of humans or flowering plants with that of sponges or red algae (such as a simple seaweed). Humans and flowering plants are manifestly more complex than sponges or red algae and have more structured bodies, with organs, transport systems and different tissues, all made up of many cells of various types. By comparison, although made up of many cells, neither sponges nor red algae have organs or transport systems, and the number of cell types is minimal. Single-celled organisms show a still more primitive condition, as all the functions of the organism have to be contained within the single cell which, by definition, can only be of one type.

If such a biological hierarchy of life has an evolutionary basis and this is reflected in the fossil record, then we would expect relatively primitive multicellular organisms such as sponges and red algae to appear before much more complex organisms such as humans and flowering plants. Similarly, we would expect single-celled organisms to appear before sponges and red algae. Fossil sponges have been known from Cambrian rocks since Sedgwick's day, but can the Precambrian fossil record be reasonably expected to contain the remains of single-celled organisms, especially as most of them have no durable hard parts and are microscopic? Another problem is that most Precambrian strata have been deeply buried, squeezed and heated at some stage in their history, and the resulting recrystallization of the rocks during metamorphism (*Atlas*, pp.171–172) destroys fossil evidence.

Despite all these difficulties, the Precambrian fossil record does indeed preserve evidence of the kind of sequence we might expect from primitive single cells to more complex multicellular organisms. Over recent decades many finds have been made in Precambrian strata, especially those in Australia and southern Africa that have not been subjected to the destructive influences of high temperatures and pressures, and such areas will surely yield many more Precambrian fossils.

- What are the oldest fossils visible to the naked eye, and how old are they?
- Stromatolites, 3500 Ma old (*Atlas*, p.53).

Stromatolites are mound-like structures formed by the activities of various bacteria. We know this because some stromatolites are still forming today in a few places. The main bacteria involved are **cyanobacteria** (formerly called 'blue–green algae'), which produce oxygen during **photosynthesis**, i.e. they use light as an energy source, carbon dioxide as a carbon source, and release oxygen into the atmosphere as a by-product. The cyanobacteria live in mat-like layers at the top of the structure, trapping sediment and forming mounds. They are single-celled organisms whose genetic material is *not* contained within a membrane to form a nucleus; the general term for all such organisms lacking a nucleus is **prokaryotes**. In addition to large-scale stromatolites, Precambrian sedimentary rocks also contain fossils of bacteria themselves: single cells and groups of cells, some joined together in chains. Many types of bacteria would have existed then, as today. Figure 2.1 compares the morphology of some living and fossil cyanobacteria; note how similar the ancient and modern ones appear to be.

According to evidence from minerals preserved in Precambrian rocks, the Earth's atmosphere originally lacked oxygen. For example, in today's oxygen-rich surroundings, the mineral uraninite (uranium oxide, an energy source for nuclear power plants) quickly dissolves and weathers away. Yet pebbles of uraninite are preserved in early Precambrian river deposits, revealing that there must have been very little atmospheric oxygen at the time, otherwise the pebbles would never have survived the processes of weathering, erosion, transport and deposition.

Eventually the atmosphere changed to being oxygen rich, probably as a result of photosynthesis by cyanobacteria. Some oxygen may also have been formed by non-biological mechanisms, such as the breakdown of water (H_2O) into hydrogen (H_2) and oxygen (O_2) by ultraviolet radiation. It was, however, not until about 2500 Ma ago that oxygen in the atmosphere slowly started to build up into permanent accumulations, reaching about 15% of its present level by 2000 Ma ago. Strata such as those shown on p.51 of the *Atlas* reveal the progressive build-up of oxygen in the

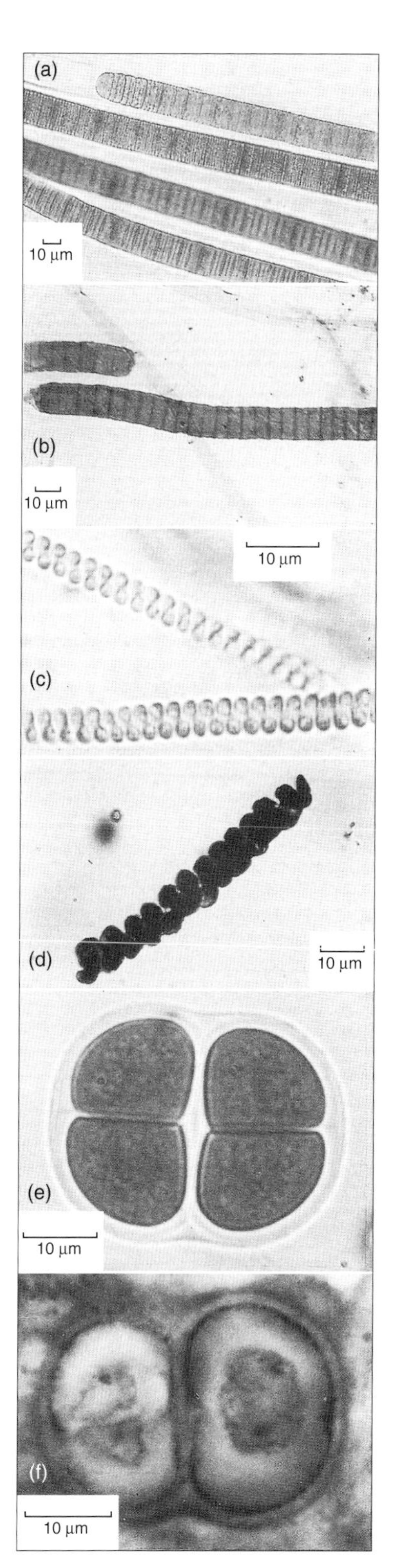

Figure 2.1 Comparison of living and fossil cyanobacteria. (a), (c) and (e) are from stromatolites growing today in Mexico; (b), (d) and (f) are from rocks in the former Soviet Union. (b) is 950 Ma old; (d) is 850 Ma old and (f) is 1550 Ma old.

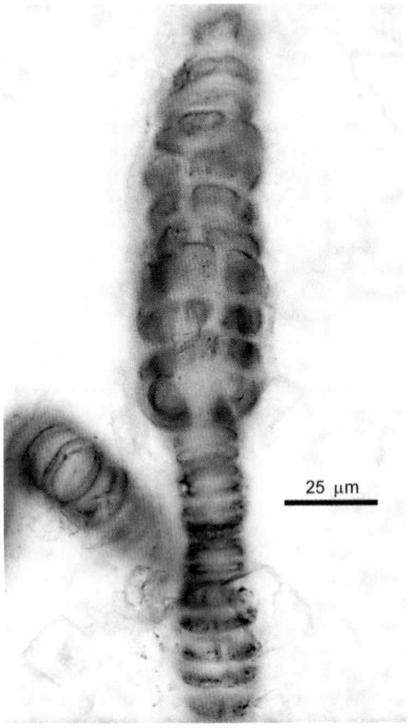

25 µm

Figure 2.2 *Bangiomorpha pubescens*, a 1200 Ma old red alga. The scale bar is 0.025 mm long (the symbol µm means a micron or micrometre, i.e. a millionth of a metre).

atmosphere. The dissolved iron that had accumulated in seawater began to combine with atmospheric oxygen to form rust, which settled to the sea bed, turning the sediments red. Some of the oxygen (O_2) was converted into ozone (O_3), forming a protective layer in the upper atmosphere that shielded life from harmful ultraviolet radiation; previously seawater alone had this protective role.

Multiplication of cells and the arrival of sex

The first cells with their genetic material enclosed in a nucleus (i.e. organisms termed **eukaryotes**, as opposed to prokaryotes) do not appear in the fossil record until about 2100 Ma ago (though evidence from molecular biology suggests they may have evolved earlier). Initially, these more advanced cells were in the main slowly evolving, photosynthetic plankton, but about 1200 Ma ago they diversified rapidly, and multicellular algae (small seaweeds) arose about this time.

The oldest known multicellular organism that can be clearly identified with a living group is a 1200 Ma old red alga called *Bangiomorpha pubescens* from arctic Canada (Figure 2.2). Fossils of this tiny filamentous alga show distinctive patterns of cell division which identify it as belonging to a particular group of red algae. It is also the oldest fossil to show evidence of sexual reproduction, i.e. a mixing of genetic material from different individuals, as opposed to the simpler and more primitive form of reproduction through asexual budding of new cells which are more or less identical to the 'parent' cell.

What benefits did the evolution of sexual reproduction bring to Precambrian life? Sexual reproduction allowed for increased genetic variation, and hence diversification of species. This led on to complex multicellularity with specialization of cells, which in turn allowed an increase in size, often a benefit in the 'struggle for life'. In other words, without sexual reproduction life would be stuck as microscopic single cells and linked chains and sheets of asexually produced, multicellular 'slime'.

Eventually, eukaryotic cells became larger, and more specialized, and with the protection from harmful radiation afforded by a thicker ozone layer, a wide variety of shallow-water environments at the edges of the oceans became accessible to them. Only in Vendian times, at the end of the Precambrian, however, did well organized, large multicellular animals appear (see below).

A note on the origin of life

Ever since the foundation of organic chemistry in the early nineteenth century, when Friedrich Wöhler first synthesized the biological compound urea in the laboratory, it has been clear that organic chemicals can be generated without the agency of living organisms. But it was another century before scientists suggested that organic molecules could have been formed in the first oceans by spontaneous non-biological processes. Furthermore, it was suggested that such molecules might have been able to reproduce themselves.

In the 1920s, a young Russian biochemist, Alexander Ivanovich Oparin (*Atlas*, p.200), observed that oils can be dispersed in water as tiny spherical droplets with a superficial resemblance to simple living cells. Oparin suggested that life began with the build-up of more and more complex molecules within such droplets, then enzymes, and finally genes (although people then had little idea what genes really were). By the 1950s, biochemists had a much better understanding of what the prerequisites for life might have been.

- From reading the *Atlas* pp.50–53, can you identify some of these prerequisites for life?

- Water at an appropriate temperature, i.e. above freezing and below boiling; the basic chemical elements of organic molecules (especially carbon, oxygen, hydrogen and nitrogen, alone or as simple inorganic compounds); energy, perhaps supplied by lightning.

In the 1950s, the American chemist Stanley Miller (*Atlas*, p.51) combined these 'ingredients' in a series of experiments which did indeed produce an impressive array of organic molecules. These included many amino acids, the basic building blocks of proteins. From such experiments the idea was developed that life perhaps began as some 'primordial soup' of amino acids and then somehow led to proteins and simple living cells. There was, however, no obvious mechanism by which this could have been achieved and, whilst today we are far nearer an understanding of the mechanisms involved, the details remain uncertain and much discussed. The synthesis of complex organic molecules was certainly a prerequisite to the early evolution of life on Earth, though possibly these molecules were brought to Earth from elsewhere by meteorites.

Now read the *Atlas*, pp.54–57. Useful tip: as we progress through the *Atlas*, you can keep track of geological time by using the globe on the timeline at the top of each two-page spread.

One of life's largest gear-changes came when, according to the fossil record, large and complex multicellular animals made their first appearance about 610 Ma ago. Life on the Earth, for the first time, now included relatively large individual organisms with a range of specialized cells (though still lacking hard parts). This group of animals, the **Ediacaran fauna**, named after Ediacara in South Australia, and found in many places around the world (including Charnwood Forest in Leicestershire, UK), was widespread by 565 Ma ago. Some of the fossils resemble modern animals such as jellyfishes, but many have a peculiar quilted structure unknown in animals today (*Atlas*, pp. 56–57). Most of these puzzling Ediacaran organisms seem to have left no descendants.

2.2 Summary of very early life

Sedimentary rocks from Greenland, 3850 Ma old, contain carbon in a form interpreted as evidence of biological activity. These chemical fossils are thought to have originated from marine bacteria or bacteria-like organisms. The implications are that life must have originated some time before this, perhaps as long ago as 4000 Ma.

From about 3500 Ma, stromatolites (mound-like structures produced mainly by cyanobacteria) became increasingly abundant in warm shallow seas. It was photosynthetic bacteria like these that produced most of the oxygen that eventually formed a permanent accumulation in the atmosphere, reaching about 15% of its present level by 2000 Ma ago.

Life probably consisted only of simple bacteria in which the genetic material was not enclosed in a nucleus (i.e. prokaryotes) until about 2100 Ma ago, when more complex cells with a nucleus (eukaryotes) first appear in the fossil record. Oil and gas (chemical fossil residues) from 2000 Ma old strata of Australia and southern Africa suggest that there were abundant microorganisms occupying seas by this time, and the Gunflint sedimentary rocks of western Ontario of about this age contain various microorganisms in which some details of the cellular structure are preserved in silica.

Multicellular algae had evolved by about 1200 Ma ago. *Bangiomorpha* (1200 Ma) is the oldest multicellular organism that can be identified as belonging to a particular group of living organisms (red algae), and its fossils reveal the first evidence of sexual reproduction.

Late in Precambrian times, from around 610 Ma ago, a variety of large, soft-bodied, marine organisms appear in the fossil record around the world. Collectively called the Ediacaran fauna, they are generally regarded as the first multicellular animals, and they include worm-like, jellyfish-like, sponge-like and other creatures of unknown relationships. By the end of the Precambrian, 545 Ma ago, all life was still confined to the sea, and almost no animals with hard parts (such as shells, skeletons or teeth) had yet appeared.

Life in the Palaeozoic

3

3.1 The Cambrian explosion

One of the most important events in the history of life began about 545 Ma ago, i.e. some four billion years after the origin of the Earth, and over 3.3 billion years after the origin of life. The term '**Cambrian explosion**' reflects a sudden burst of evolution, when a wide variety of organisms, especially those with hard, mineralized parts, first appear in the fossil record. Thus began the Phanerozoic Eon — 'the time of visible life' — and the Palaeozoic Era.

Now read the *Atlas*, pp.58–61.

At the start of the Cambrian Period, body fossils with hard shelly parts became abundant for the first time. Actually, the very first evidence of preservable hard parts comes from some tiny fossils, including tubes made of calcium carbonate about 0.2 mm across, found in late Precambrian strata about 550 Ma old. The unknown organisms that produced them were living at the same time as the Ediacaran fauna.

- What, in general, was different about the size of fossils with hard shelly parts in the earliest Cambrian, compared with late Precambrian life such as the Ediacaran organisms?

- The fossils with hard shelly parts were much smaller (*Atlas*, p.60).

A wide variety of small (1–2 mm) shelly fossils appeared in the earliest part of the Cambrian Period — assorted shapes such as tubes and cones, as well as spines, scales, and knobs (*Atlas*, pp.58–59). It's often difficult to tell whether a fossil is the complete skeleton of a single organism or an isolated part of some larger creature. The soft tissues associated with these hard parts are almost entirely unknown, and the reconstructions of soft parts shown in the *Atlas* (pp.60–61) are conjectural.

- What seems likely to have been the main stimulus for the acquisition of hard parts by organisms in the earliest Cambrian?

- The need for protection (*Atlas*, pp.60–61).

Protection from predation or other damage is certainly consistent with the first appearance of defensive structures such as spines and scales, and tubes and conical shells that could protect vulnerable soft parts inside. There are, however, a number of other possible reasons why hard parts first evolved, as discussed in the *Atlas*, p.61, some or all of which may have been involved.

- A greatly increased variety of types of trace fossils, especially burrows of soft-bodied animals, are found around the start of the Cambrian Period. Bearing in mind what trace fossils are (Section 1.2), what is the significance of this finding?

- It reflects the evolution of more complex patterns of activity and behaviour, some of it probably related to the avoidance of predators.

Although environmental changes were occurring (such as a rise in global sea level (*Atlas*, p.58), there is, to date, little evidence of special, widespread environmental changes that could have directly triggered the Cambrian explosion. Whatever the causes, once triggered, a wide range of ecological opportunities presumably became available for exploitation, promoting the rapid evolution of new, quite different types of animals. By about 530 Ma, most of the animal phyla that are in existence today had appeared. Not surprisingly, a few entirely soft-bodied phyla living today have no known fossil record, so we don't know when they evolved. Evidence from genetics (*Atlas*, p.187) suggests that some animal phyla had diverged from each other much earlier than the start of the Cambrian explosion, but the timing remains uncertain.

Many of the newly evolved Cambrian phyla show organization of the body into specialized areas — especially a head end with food-trapping and sensory organs, a tubular gut and limbs. There is no doubt that many Cambrian animals were equipped with adaptations for preying on other animals, and were able to pursue food much more actively than could the Ediacaran fauna — such as by scuttling over the sea floor, swimming actively, and burrowing. Note that all forms of life (except possibly a few algae, Section 3.7) were as yet confined to the sea.

Although many types of the small shelly fossils disappear from the fossil record soon after the start of the Cambrian, some are thought to have been molluscs at an early evolutionary stage, in which case they did leave descendants.

3.1.1 The Burgess Shale

High in the Canadian Rockies is exposed a deposit of middle Cambrian age, about 530 Ma old, called the Burgess Shale. It contains the fossils of animals that lived on a muddy sea floor, and which were suddenly transported into deeper, oxygen-poor water by submarine landslides. Their catastrophic burial has given us an exceptional view of Cambrian life. Not only have animals with hard shelly parts been preserved but entirely soft-bodied forms are also preserved as thin films on the sediment surface.

Now read the *Atlas*, pp.62–65.

Some of the most common Cambrian fossils, which appear immediately after the first shelly fossils, are trilobites. These were a group of exclusively marine arthropods, members of the enormously diverse phylum of animals with jointed, external skeletons that today include forms such as crabs, lobsters, insects and spiders. The trilobite fossils of the Burgess Shale are like many trilobites found elsewhere but exceptional in that not only is the main part of their outer skeleton (or exoskeleton) preserved, but so too are their appendages such as antennae and legs (see, for example, those of *Olenoides*, *Atlas*, p.63). Elsewhere, trilobite appendages are extremely rare as they were poorly mineralized. We will study trilobites in more detail shortly. Other types of arthropods, especially ones lacking well-mineralized exoskeletons (such as *Marrella*, *Atlas*, p.60), are particularly abundant in the Burgess Shale.

Only about 15% of the 120 genera present in the Burgess Shale are shelly organisms such as trilobites and brachiopods that dominate typical Cambrian fossil **assemblages** (fossils that occur together) elsewhere. The shelly component was therefore in a minority, and organisms with hard parts probably formed less than 5% of individuals in the living community.

If the soft-bodied fossils of the Burgess Shale are taken away, all that remains is a typical Cambrian assemblage of hard-bodied organisms. Why is this important to bear in mind when trying to interpret other Cambrian fossil assemblages?

- The other Cambrian assemblages may also have been dominated by soft-bodied animals, even if the only fossils they now contain are of hard-bodied ones.

Another important revelation of the Burgess Shale lies in the wide diversity of animal types that were around in middle Cambrian time, about 530 Ma ago. There are representatives of about a dozen of the phyla that persist to the present day. One form closely related to early arthropods was *Anomalocaris*, the largest known Cambrian animal, some individuals of which may have reached two metres in length. Its extraordinary jaw (*Atlas*, p.65) consisted of spiny plates encircling the mouth, which probably constricted down on prey in much the same way that the plates of an iris diaphragm cut down the light in a camera. This fearsome mouth is seen in place in the reconstruction of the closely related *Laggania* (*Atlas*, pp.64–65). Note that the colours of organisms shown in this and other such reconstructions are conjectural.

About a dozen types of Burgess Shale fossils have been said to be so unlike anything living today and so different from each other that, had they been living now, each would have been placed in a separate phylum. With further study, however, the relationships of these puzzling animals (such as *Hallucigenia*, *Atlas*, p.63) are becoming clearer. It seems that some Burgess Shale forms are hard to classify simply because the boundaries between major categories of animal life were still blurred shortly after the Cambrian explosion. In other words, by mid Cambrian time, there still had not been enough time for some groups to have diverged sufficiently from their recent common ancestors to be distinctly different.

Burgess Shale-type faunas have been found in about 30 sites ranging from North America and Greenland, to China and Australia. The wide range of animals they contain seems to reflect an unpruned 'bush of diversity' resulting from the Cambrian explosion. Not long after, though, extinction lopped off some of the branches, leaving phyla with the relatively distinct features that have remained to this day.

3.1.2 An overview of animal phyla

We have already met quite a few different animal phyla, and it's useful to get an overview of all the ones commonly found in the fossil record and their mode of life before studying some in more detail. Except for a few soft-bodied phyla with very poor fossil records, it is clear that all the animal phyla had appeared by the Ordovician Period.

The following terms are very useful for describing the mode of life and the environmental setting of organisms. The terms are explained here as they are applied to marine organisms, but they are also sometimes applied to organisms living in lakes.

benthic — animals and plants that live on the sea floor; collective noun: **benthos**.

pelagic — animals and plants that live above the sea floor. They may be either **nektonic** (animals only) or **planktonic** (animals and plants).

nektonic — animals that swim actively (e.g. fish, squid); collective noun: **nekton**.

planktonic — animals and plants that drift passively or swim feebly, mainly in the surface waters of seas; collective noun: **plankton**. The term includes **phytoplankton** (photosynthetic organisms, mostly algae) and **zooplankton** (mostly microscopic animals, including larvae of larger ones, but also some macroscopic animals that are readily visible with the naked eye, e.g. jellyfish).

epifaunal — animals that live on the sea floor, either on soft sediment, or attached to rocks, seaweed, etc. (**sessile**), or that move over the sea floor (**vagrant**); collective noun: **epifauna**.

infaunal — animals that live within sediment, often in burrows or borings into harder material; collective noun **infauna**.

Like most classifications involving living organisms, some invertebrates do not fit neatly into these categories, e.g. the common prawn buries itself in sediment during the day (i.e. is infaunal), but at night emerges to join the epifauna as it feeds. Other epifaunal animals bury themselves during low tide.

Box 3.1 gives some key points about the important animal phyla most commonly found in the fossil record. You will often need to refer to this useful summary. Figure 3.1 shows typical fossil representatives of some of the phyla in Box 3.1.

Box 3.1 Common phyla in the fossil record

Some key points about the important animal phyla most commonly found in the fossil record. The age range and mode of life of some common groups are given. Phyla that are microscopic throughout life are excluded.

Porifera. Sponges. Cambrian to Recent. Mainly marine; some freshwater. Sessile. The simplest multicellular animals, sponges lack definite tissues and organs, e.g. they have no nervous system. They have a skeleton of calcium carbonate, silica, or, as in some bath sponges, horny organic material. Water passes in through the sponge's many surface pores, often to the central cavity of a sack-like body, and out through a large hole at the top. Some have a stalk (Figure 3.1a), others are encrusting and irregular in shape. Sponges feed by filtering off minute organic particles from the water. Sponges are locally abundant fossils, especially in Cretaceous rocks, where they are very commonly enclosed in flint nodules in the Chalk.

Cnidaria (pronounced with a silent 'C': 'nigh-dare-ee-a'). Late Precambrian (Ediacaran) to Recent. Almost entirely marine. Cnidarians have a central mouth around which are stinging tentacles for catching prey. By far the most important fossil group are the entirely marine, generally benthic, **corals**, which secrete a skeleton of calcium carbonate below the soft, anemone-like parts at the top. Corals may be either colonial (with many genetically identical, linked individuals sharing a skeleton) or solitary individuals. There are three main groups of corals: rugose corals (solitary, Figure 3.1b, or colonial), Ordovician to Permian; tabulate corals (always colonial), Ordovician to Permian; and scleractinian corals, sometimes also called hexacorals (solitary or colonial), Triassic to Recent. **Sea anemones** and **jellyfish** are also cnidarians, but being soft-bodied these groups are much less common in the fossil record.

Bryozoa. Bryozoans. Ordovician to Recent. Sometimes called 'moss animals'. Normally marine, rarely freshwater. Sessile, tiny animals which live in colonies, with a skeleton usually of calcium carbonate. The colonies vary in shape; some are encrusting sheets ('sea mats'), others may be delicate net-like fronds (Figure 3.1c) or branching twigs. Each colony consists of a few to thousands of interconnected individuals. When feeding, tentacles filter microorganisms from the water. Bryozoans often occur as fossils among the diverse fauna of reefs. Some bryozoans look rather like small corals; a few species can look a little like graptolites (see below).

Brachiopoda. Brachiopods (pronounced 'bracky-o-pods'). Cambrian to Recent. Entirely marine, benthic animals. Sometimes called 'lamp-shells' (after their resemblance to Roman oil lamps). Brachiopods are typically 2–5 cm long, but they range in size from a few mm to as much as 30 cm. The shell, which encloses the soft tissues, has two parts, called valves. One valve is almost always larger than the other. Many brachiopods are attached to the sea floor by a stalk of horn-like or fleshy material, the pedicle; in fossil brachiopods the presence of this pedicle is indicated by a hole passing through the larger of the two valves (Figure 3.1d). Some are free-lying on the sea floor, and a few are cemented or attached by spines. In most brachiopods the shell is composed of calcium carbonate, though some are phosphatic. They feed by drawing water into the shell and filtering off food particles with a complex feeding device called a lophophore. Brachiopods are much less abundant and diverse today than during the Palaeozoic and Mesozoic. They are the commonest fossil in many Palaeozoic shallow marine limestones and shales. About 20 species occur today off the British Isles, mostly in deeper waters, and are rarely seen.

Mollusca. Molluscs. Cambrian to Recent. Mainly marine. A very diverse phylum, perhaps numerically the most abundant large invertebrates in the fossil record. There are shelled and unshelled forms. Although at first the six or so living classes may seem unrelated, they represent evolutionary variations on the same theme — the molluscan bodyplan. Three classes, each of which range from Cambrian to Recent, are particularly important, both as fossils and today: the Bivalvia — **bivalves** (e.g. cockles, mussels and oysters) (Figure 3.1e); the Gastropoda — **gastropods** (e.g. slugs and snails); and the nektonic Cephalopoda — **cephalopods** (e.g. squid, cuttlefish, octopus and nautilus). Most bivalves are marine (vagrant to sessile benthos), though some are freshwater. The majority of gastropods are aquatic, and most of these live in shallow seas, but they are also widespread in freshwater and on dry land. Cephalopods are (and have been) entirely marine, and are the most highly evolved molluscs. The most important fossil cephalopod groups are all forms with chambered shells — the **nautiloids** (Cambrian to Recent), the familiar spiral-shelled **ammonites** (Triassic to Cretaceous), and the bullet-shaped **belemnites** (Jurassic to Cretaceous).

Echinodermata. Echinoderms. Cambrian to Recent. Entirely marine. Most are benthic. Many are vagrant, some are sessile, and a few are free-swimming (nektonic). Most echinoderm skeletons are made of many porous plates of calcite (calcium carbonate) which are very thinly covered with soft tissue. Multipurpose, extendible tentacles called tube feet emerge to the outside, and are used especially in feeding, respiration and locomotion. In many forms there is a distinctive five-rayed arrangement of plates and tube feet. Echinoderm means 'spiny skin', referring to the fact that some groups have spines or hard, warty bumps projecting from the surface. The most common fossil groups are **sea urchins** (**echinoids**), Ordovician to Recent, and **sea lilies** (**crinoids**), Cambrian to Recent. Two other well-known living groups, both Ordovician to Recent, are **starfish** (**asteroids**) and **brittle stars** (**ophiuroids**). There are also several extinct groups.

Arthropoda. Arthropods. Cambrian to Recent. The largest phylum of animals, with a great diversity of morphology and mode of life; living forms are found in most possible habitats in water and on land. A partial list of groups includes **crustaceans** (**crabs**, **lobsters**, **barnacles** and **shrimps**), **insects**, **millipedes**, **centipedes**, **spiders**, **king crabs**, **scorpions**, **mites** and

Figure 3.1 Representative fossils of some of the phyla mentioned in Box 3.1. (a) A sponge, *Siphonia tulipa*, Cretaceous (5.5 cm). (b) A cnidarian, the solitary rugose coral *Clisiophyllum*, Carboniferous (3.5 cm). (c) A bryozoan, *Fenestella plebeia*, Carboniferous (field of view 3 cm). (d) A brachiopod, *Terebratula gigantea*, Cretaceous (4 cm). (e) A mollusc, the bivalve *Pleuromya costata*, Jurassic (4.5 cm). (f) A hemichordate, the graptolite *Hustedograptus teretiusculus*, Ordovician (2.5 cm).

several extinct groups, of which the entirely marine, extinct **trilobites** (pronounced 'try-lo-bites') are the most important. The most characteristic features of the phylum are the hard outer coating (exoskeleton) which is divided into segments, and the paired, jointed appendages which vary in number and function. The exoskeleton, usually of chitin (a strong, lightweight organic material), may be further strengthened by calcium carbonate or calcium phosphate, increasing the preservation potential. Growth occurs during periodic moulting when the exoskeleton is shed and a new, larger one is formed.

Hemichordata*. Hemichordates. Cambrian to Recent. By far the most important fossil group are the **graptolites** — extinct, entirely marine colonies confined to the Palaeozoic Era, particularly abundant in Ordovician and Silurian rocks where they are very useful zone fossils. Many look like saw blades a few centimetres long on the rock, with 'teeth' on one or both sides of the 'saw' (Figure 3.1f). The 'teeth' were actually tiny cups that housed individuals which made up the colony and possessed filter-feeding tentacles. Some graptolites were benthic and sessile, but most were pelagic, either drifting or possibly swimming feebly as part of the zooplankton.

*Some biologists place the hemichordates as a subphylum within the Phylum Chordata.

Chordata. Chordates. Cambrian to Recent. All chordates possess a notochord (a flexible rod running along the length of the body). Minor living chordate groups, lacking a vertebral column (backbone), include sea squirts and the lancelet. The major group are the **vertebrates**, which have bony or cartilaginous skeletons and a head. Today, vertebrates include five classes: **fish** (Cambrian to Recent), **amphibians** (Devonian to Recent), **reptiles** (Carboniferous to Recent), **mammals** (Triassic to Recent) and **birds** (Jurassic to Recent). Important extinct reptile groups include the land-dwelling **dinosaurs** (Triassic to Cretaceous), the marine **ichthyosaurs** (Triassic to Cretaceous) and **plesiosaurs** (Jurassic to Cretaceous), and the flying **pterosaurs** (Triassic to Cretaceous). Vertebrate fossils are relatively rare compared with invertebrates, and are usually only fragments.

3.1.3 The origin of the vertebrates

Vertebrates such as ourselves are by definition animals with a backbone (or vertebral column, *Atlas G*, p.215), paired limbs, a skull and various other structures. Until recently vertebrates were thought to extend back only into late Ordovician times, some 450 million years ago. At this time fossils of strange-looking fish with bony headshields, such as *Sacabambaspis* (*Atlas*, pp.70–71), appear in the fossil record. These jawless fish (called **agnathans**, see *Atlas G*, p.204) are only very distantly related to the sole living agnathans, the lampreys and hagfish. However, these Ordovician creatures are already highly evolved and clearly had yet more ancient ancestors.

To understand what such ancestors might have been like we need to consider the backbone — the fundamental vertebrate feature — in a bit more detail. The precursor to the backbone is a stiffening rod, called the **notochord** (*Atlas G*, p.212), details of which we know from the study of developing vertebrate embryos and the few surviving animals which have retained a notochord, such as the lancelet *Branchiostoma*.

Now read the *Atlas*, pp.66–67.

What is the main function of the notochord?

It lengthens and stiffens the body, allowing the blocks of muscles to flex the body sideways into zigzag bends for swimming (*Atlas*, p.66).

The fundamental chordate characteristic of a notochord (Box 3.1) has now been identified in various Cambrian fossils, such as *Pikaia* from the Burgess Shale (Section 3.1.1).

- Why is *Pikaia* classified as a chordate but not a vertebrate?

- It has a notochord but not a backbone, nor other vertebrate features such as paired limbs (*Atlas*, pp.66–67).

The extinct **conodonts** (late Cambrian to end Triassic in age) have been shown to possess not only a notochord but also tooth structures and paired eyes, which seem to suggest that they were more advanced than chordates such as *Pikaia* and close to the earliest vertebrates. (You will read about conodonts shortly on p.70 of the *Atlas*.) Some early Cambrian fossils recently found in China are thought to preserve all the basic chordate features plus some more advanced vertebrate ones, namely gills as well as paired eyes. If so, then it is clear that some animals close to the vertebrate bodyplan had already appeared by early Cambrian times, and chordate ancestry probably reaches back into the late Precambrian.

Question 3.1 Humans belong to the vertebrate group known as mammals. Using Box 3.1 or the summary chart on p.164 of the *Atlas*, place mammals and the other four main vertebrate groups in order of their evolutionary appearance. ◀

3.2 The Ordovician seas

Read the *Atlas*, pp.68–71.

Collecting seashells on an Ordovician beach would have been a rather curious experience. Whilst most shells were made of similar materials to those found on a modern beach, the detailed form of many would have been quite unfamiliar, and all the species have long been extinct.

Have a look at the panoramic illustration on pp.70–71 of the *Atlas*. From this and the *Atlas*, pp.68–71, think about which organisms appear most unfamiliar to you.

There are many organisms that probably seem unfamiliar, and when reading about them you may want to refer to Box 3.1. Brachiopods, e.g. *Strophomena*, are superficially clam-like animals, and although not extinct, are much rarer now than in the Palaeozoic; most people have never seen a living one. Graptolites, e.g. *Orthograptus*, are extinct colonial animals that mostly drifted in the ocean currents (Figure 3.2). Trilobites, e.g. *Triarthrus*, are extinct marine arthropods (see also Activity 3.1 below). Conodonts, e.g. *Promissum*, are extinct, and jawless (agnathan) fish, e.g. *Sacabambaspis*, are extinct except for hagfish and lampreys (see Section 3.1.3 above). The straight-shelled nautiloid cephalopods, e.g. *Endoceras*, are extinct and only distantly related to today's *Nautilus*, which has a spiral shell. The groups still very much with us include horseshoe crabs, snails (gastropods), e.g. *Cyclonema*, and corals (although Palaeozoic corals were significantly different from modern corals; see Activity 3.1). Bivalves (not shown) were much rarer in the Ordovician seas than they are today.

Figure 3.2 Specimens of the graptolite *Diplograptus* in Ordovician shales (field of view 3.5 cm). Graptolites often look like tiny saw blades lying on the rock surface.

All this fauna was marine. Very little, if any, animal life had made it out of the sea onto dry land by the end of the Ordovician. Trace fossils of an unknown, possibly millipede-like animal (*Atlas*, p.71) are rare evidence that invertebrates were exploring the edge of the land by a freshwater route. There is fossil evidence that bryophyte-like plants (*Atlas G*, p.205) and fungi had begun to colonize land environments back in Ordovician times (Section 3.7). Apart from a small advance guard, however, the main invasion of freshwater and land environments by plants and animals did not really get going until the Silurian Period.

3.3 The Silurian Period and the invasion of the land

Read the *Atlas*, pp.72–75.

What global event had reduced global sea level at the end of Ordovician times, drastically affecting shallow marine organisms, and leaving the diversity of early Silurian life severely curtailed?

The global climate descended into an ice age, locking up ocean water in the polar ice caps, exposing much of the continental shelves above sea level, eliminating many shallow marine habitats and driving many species to extinction (*Atlas*, p.69). (Sea level probably fell by about 100 m, not 330 m as stated in the *Atlas*.)

Recent research shows that minor glaciations continued into the early Silurian, but after a while the oceans became warmer again and sea levels rose. It took several million years for marine life to recover. At first, stromatolites (Section 2.1) were relatively common, apparently because the organisms that normally suppressed them had suffered severely, but by mid Silurian times, vast coral reefs were established in tropical waters, promoting a rich diversity of organisms. The growth of corals with their tough, mineralized skeletons turns flat sea beds into complex 3-D topographies, baffling ocean currents, and providing sheltered surfaces and new ecological niches (see *Atlas G*, p.212). We will soon study some of the organisms that thrived in such environments.

Meanwhile, the animals and plants that were invading the land faced all sorts of environmental challenges to which they had to adapt. For example, if a marine plant cell is directly surrounded by fresh water, the water tends to flow into it by the process of **osmosis**, causing it to burst. Alternatively, if the cell is directly surrounded by air, it loses all its water, just as seaweeds become hard and crisp when stranded above high tide and exposed to the wind and the sun. So, to survive in air, plants had to acquire an effective outer coat to keep the right amount of water in. They also had to evolve small, controllable pores to enable gases to be exchanged through this coat. Expressed this way, it is all too easy to give the impression, quite wrongly, that such innovations could be achieved intentionally, almost as if by some directed effort. On the contrary, as in all evolutionary explanations, natural selection would have favoured those organisms that were, *by chance*, better adapted to these new environmental challenges (Section 1.7).

Without the buoyancy provided by immersion in water, adaptations in both plants and animals were needed to support a body on land against the pull of gravity. The relatively high density of water provides much greater support for the bodies of marine organisms than does less dense air — hence the expression 'like a fish out of water'. To grow up off the land surface, plants had to develop groups of special plumbing cells to conduct water, nutrients and the products of photosynthesis around their bodies. Only about 4 cm tall, *Cooksonia* (see Figure 3.3a and illustration, *Atlas*, p.75) lacked leaves, and sent short, forking shoots upward to capture sunlight and release **spores** (reproductive cells) into the wind. These first true **vascular land plants** (*Atlas G*, p.215) with specialized cells for carrying fluids around an upright plant were still dependent on water for reproduction, and lived in swamps and on riverbanks and floodplains. The earliest movement onto land, for both plants and animals, seems to have been through the medium of fresh, as opposed to saline, water.

(a)

Air, being a gas, has a low capacity to store heat compared with seawater and, to survive, life on land must be able to withstand relatively large temperature fluctuations as well as higher amounts of ultraviolet radiation from the Sun. Exchange of gametes during reproduction is also much easier in water where male gametes can swim to fertilize the female ones. The animals that, by chance, were best adapted to life on land were the arthropods. They were very strong for their size, and already had an almost waterproof outer skeleton that was resistant to damage by ultraviolet light. Numerous paired and jointed limbs with internal muscles helped overcome gravity and allow movement over uneven terrestrial surfaces. However, the arthropods could not have invaded the land if there had not already been some supply of food there.

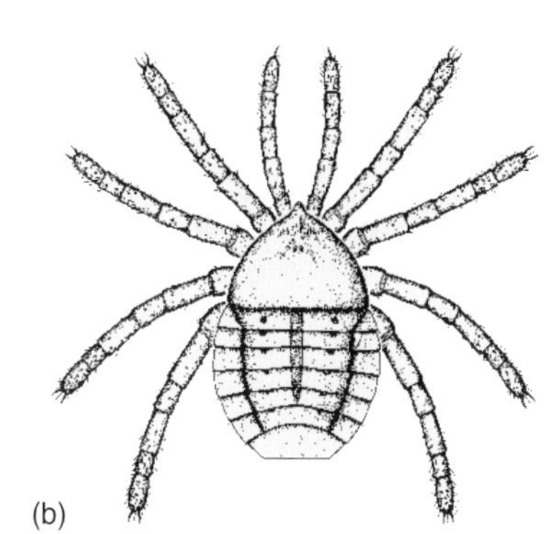

(b)

Figure 3.3 Early life on land. (a) *Cooksonia*, a very early land plant from Silurian rocks in Wales, about 4 cm tall. Notice the spore-bearing structures at the end of each simple-branching stem. (b) One of the earliest known land animals — a spider-like creature (4 mm long including legs) from Silurian rocks in Shropshire, England.

- According to the *Atlas* (p.74), what are the first arthropods believed to have eaten?

- The first arthropods were probably eating the decaying remains of plants such as *Cooksonia*.

Once the greening of the land had begun, small millipedes and wingless insects were apparently tempted onto it to eat the rotting plant debris, and they and their remains were eaten in turn by predatory or scavenging carnivorous arthropods such as centipedes, scorpions and small spider-like creatures (Figure 3.3b).

3.4 Life in the Silurian sea

As we've seen, the Cambrian explosion left the seas teeming with a huge variety of animals. In the following activity you will study some of the marine life at one particular time in the Palaeozoic Era — the middle part of the Silurian Period, 430 Ma ago. You'll look in detail at two fossils which come from a deposit in the UK called the Wenlock Limestone, famous for its many beautiful fossils. The Wenlock Limestone crops out mainly around Birmingham and the borders of Wales.

The ability to make accurate observations is the most fundamental skill in any science, and for palaeontology there is no better training than studying three-dimensional fossils, and making drawings to record your observations. The replicas of fossil specimens in the Kit will help you to develop these observational skills, and train you to make inferences about the biology, mode of life and environment of extinct species.

Activity 3.1 Fossils from the Wenlock Limestone

The estimated time for this Activity is about 2 hours.

Aims

1. To examine and interpret the features of two fossil replicas, in order to understand aspects of the biology of the organisms represented, and to use this evidence to reconstruct the Silurian environment in which they lived.
2. To develop the practical science skills of observation and recording of information from three-dimensional specimens — in this case fossils — using annotated drawings.
3. To study briefly some other fossil groups common in the Silurian, especially corals.

Equipment

Kit items
Fossil replicas A and B
Hand lens

Non-Kit items
Pencil, ruler, eraser

Important advice

There is no need to spend ages on your drawings. Use simple lines and avoid elaborate shading. *Draw only in pencil*, so that you can rub out and do bits again if necessary. Sometimes, a few small gas bubbles (now round holes) may have become trapped during the making of a replica; if so, please ignore them.

When using a hand lens, you should ensure that the specimen is well lit, with the light shining onto the specimen from the left or right ahead of you. Bring both the hand lens *and* the specimen up as close to your eyes as is comfortable for focusing. Experiment a bit to see what works best.

Practical procedure

Task 1 Observations of fossil A

Take the replica of fossil A and examine it for a minute or so, first with the naked eye, and then with your hand lens.

Fossil A is a trilobite. Trilobites were a major group of entirely marine arthropods that thrived in the seas of the Palaeozoic Era and eventually became extinct in the Permian Period. The arthropods are an immensely diverse phylum (see Box 3.1). Their external jointed skeleton (exoskeleton) forms a robust armour-plating for the body, though it is flexible at the joints to allow movement.

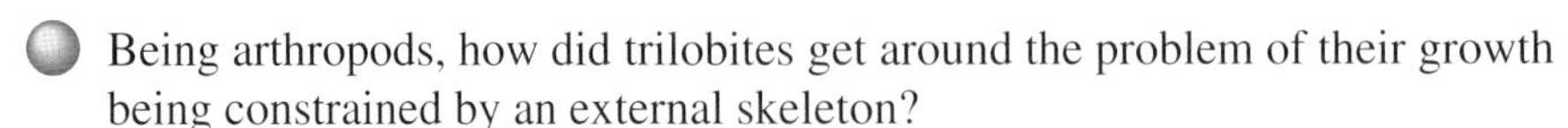

- Being arthropods, how did trilobites get around the problem of their growth being constrained by an external skeleton?

- Trilobites, like other arthropods, grew by moulting, i.e. periodically casting off their rigid outer shell, and secreting a new, larger one (Box 3.1).

Trilobites are so named because they have three lobes running up and down their length — a central axis, and two lobes: one on either side. They are also divided cross-ways into a **headshield**, a **trunk**, and a **tailpiece**. Have a preliminary look at fossil A to see if you can identify these divisions. The trunk has a number of separate segments, and the tailpiece is made of a single plate. The more formal names for the three main divisions of the trilobite body, often used elsewhere, are as follows: headshield = cephalon; trunk = thorax; tailpiece = pygidium.

Trilobites also had appendages such as antennae and legs, but these are extremely rarely found. An example where legs are preserved is shown on p.63 of the *Atlas*.

- What does the rarity of trilobite appendages suggest about their structure?

- They were not so durable, being less mineralized than the components normally found (headshield, trunk and tailpiece), and soon decayed like other soft tissues.

Now finish the partially completed drawings of this fossil in Figure 3.4, using your hand lens to observe the details. There are two views of the fossil at the same scale, one from above (a) and one from the left-hand side (b). Draw a scale bar (like that on Figure 3.5) to indicate the extent of 1 cm on the specimen. *Remember: do not spend ages on your drawings; just use simple lines and avoid fancy artistic impressions.* Label your drawing of trilobite A with its generic name, *Dalmanites*.

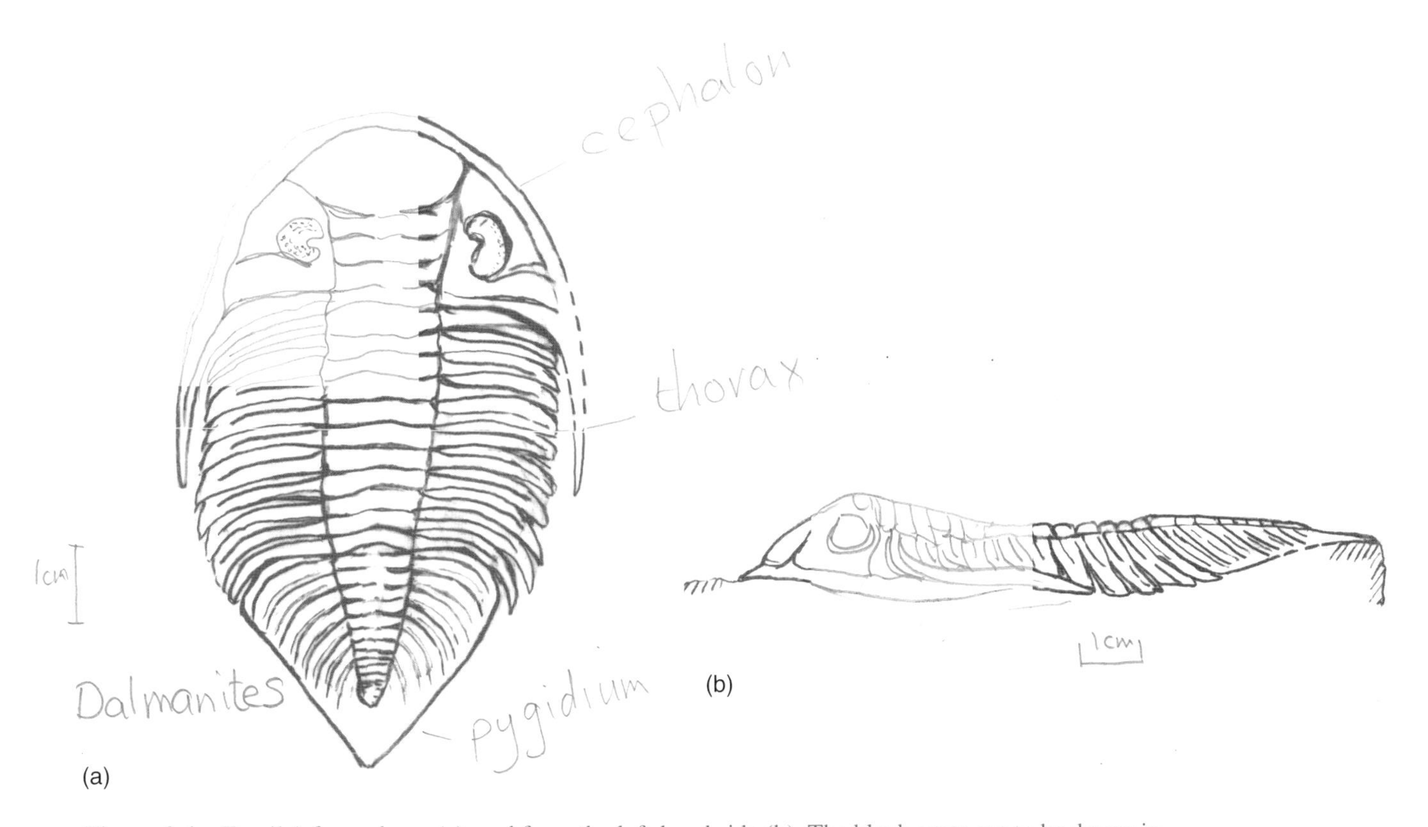

Figure 3.4 Fossil A from above (a), and from the left-hand side (b). The blank areas are to be drawn in.

Study Figure 3.5, which shows another trilobite from the Wenlock Limestone, called *Calymene* ('kal-iminny'). You should decide which labelled parts of *Calymene* correspond to those of *Dalmanites*, and then label your completed drawings of *Dalmanites* accordingly with the same terms (i.e. headshield, etc.). When drawing lines across to mark the boundaries between the headshield and trunk, and trunk and tailpiece, align these lines with where these boundaries occur at the centre of the axis, not at the outer edges of the exoskeleton. In addition, label the obvious 'spine at rear of headshield'. Both the replica and Figure 3.5 represent full-grown adults.

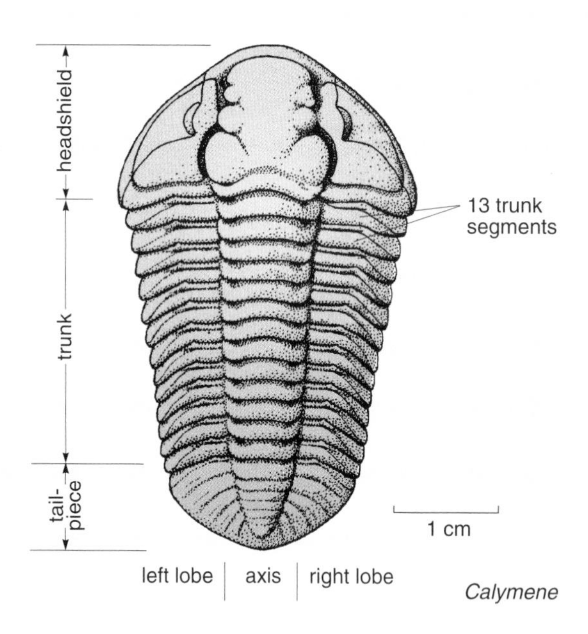

Figure 3.5 *Calymene*, a trilobite from the Wenlock Limestone.

- Which has more trunk segments, *Dalmanites* or *Calymene*?

- *Dalmanites* has 11 segments, *Calymene* has 13. If you got this wrong, look again; you may have misidentified where the trunk begins and ends. Label the number of trunk segments on Figure 3.4.

Because trilobites cast off their shell during moulting, most trilobite fossils are actually shed shells, rather than carcasses (dead animals). The trilobite's hard outer shell needed places of weakness along which it could break apart during moulting, a bit like having weak areas between the pieces of a bar of chocolate. There were lines of weakness between the headshield and the front of the trunk; between any two trunk segments; and between the end of the trunk and the front of the tailpiece. Trilobites also had one or more lines of weakness within the headshield. Figure 3.5 shows these lines of weakness for *Calymene*; they allowed two side pieces to detach from the larger, central part of the headshield. *Dalmanites* had a similar arrangement but only parts of these lines of weakness (to the side of the rear of the eyes) are clearly visible in the replica. Note that part of the trunk to the front right of the tailpiece has become crushed at some stage (post-mortem), slightly distorting the exoskeleton's original symmetry.

- Do you think it more likely that fossil A is a carcass or a moult?

- It is more likely to be a carcass than a moult because the skeleton is not split up into separate pieces.

- Use your hand lens to look at one of the two crescent-shaped, upstanding areas on either side of the head of fossil A. What structures do you think they represent?
- They are eyes.

The tiny bumps arranged in rows on each crescent are, amazing as it may seem, the lenses of an eye. The eyes were rather like the compound eyes of a modern fly (another arthropod) in having many lenses. Each trilobite lens was made of calcite, and its preservation potential was as good as the rest of the skeleton (also made mostly of calcite). Trilobites had the earliest recorded eyes in the animal world. Label the compound eyes of *Dalmanites* and of *Calymene* (Figure 3.5).

- Try to estimate very approximately the number of lenses in an eye of *Dalmanites* without counting them all. Is the number of lenses nearest to 10, 50, or 200? The left eye is better preserved, though note the lenses in the upper part have been worn away.
- The number of lenses in each eye is nearer to 200 than 10 or 50. (As the lenses are evenly spaced, you could have counted, for example, about a quarter of the eye surface and then multiplied by four.)

The presence of well-developed eyes suggests that wherever the trilobites were living there was enough light to see by, and, as light fades with depth, the water is unlikely to have been very deep.

- Trilobites that, according to independent evidence, spent a lot of time swimming well above the sea floor had eyes that extended downwards, around the side of the head, and onto the underside. Is this the case with *Dalmanites*? Examine the directions that its banks of lenses are facing.
- No. Although its eyes cover a large field of view (together they could see around a complete circle of 360 degrees in the plane of the body), the lenses were not directed downwards and underneath (except when its head was tilted).

It is therefore likely that *Dalmanites* (and *Calymene*) spent more time scuttling around on the sea floor than swimming high up in the water. They probably rested on the sea floor, stretched out in the same way as in fossil A and the specimen in Figure 3.5. These trilobites probably ate small organisms and organic debris on or near the sea floor.

Some trilobites could roll up, tucking the tail snugly underneath the head. Figure 3.6 shows a specimen of *Calymene* that has rolled itself up into a ball, like a pill bug (a type of woodlouse, another arthropod) can do. The flat, outer edges of the trunk segments had to slide over each other to enable the trilobite to roll up. *Dalmanites* could also roll up, though the tailpiece was not so snug-fitting under the head.

Figure 3.6 A specimen of *Calymene blumenbachi* from the Wenlock Limestone that rolled itself up into a ball (2.5 cm).

- Why might the ability to roll up be useful?
- It would protect any soft parts underneath the hard external skeleton from attack by predators, damage during storms, etc.

Finally, to check your completed Figure 3.4, compare it with Figure 3.29 in the 'Comments on activities' section at the end of this book.

In summary, you have been able to observe various features of the morphology of an extinct organism, and infer aspects of its mode of life and environment. You have done this by making observations, and comparing observed features with what is known of living relatives and similar fossils. In practice, when studying fossils one would also take other information into account, such as evidence from the sediment enclosing the fossil, and so on. The result is always an *interpretation* that reflects the balance of probabilities from the available information, rather than the certain truth.

More on trilobites

Many thousands of trilobite species are known, mostly from Cambrian to Silurian rocks, and all were confined to the Palaeozoic Era. By the time trilobites became extinct in the late Permian, their diversity had dwindled to a small number of species, and the group was long past its peak. The variation in trilobite form is enormous, but the basic three-lobed division of the exoskeleton is always present. The number of trunk segments varies from 2 to 40. Not all have eyes. Most are about 2–10 cm in length but some are 1–2 mm and a few species grew to nearly 1 m long. The majority of trilobites lived on or near the floor of shallow seas, but some trilobites swam in the surface waters of the open ocean, and some were adapted to low concentrations of oxygen in water hundreds of metres deep. How they reproduced is not clear. Figure 3.7 shows a range of trilobites from the Ordovician Period.

(a)

(c)

(b)

(d)

Figure 3.7 A selection of Ordovician trilobites from central Wales.
(a) *Oygiocarella* (7.5 cm).
(b) *Cnemidopyge* (3 cm).
(c) *Telaeomarrolithus* (2 cm). Trilobites like this with a pitted fringe around the head are called trinucleids. The main function of the fringe, which has tiny holes at the centre of each little pit, may have been to allow water to pass out from a feeding chamber underneath the head after the animal had strained off small food particles. This specimen is enrolled — the tailpiece, along which the specimen has partly split, is tucked up underneath the headshield.
(d) *Segmentagnostus*. This trilobite, about 1 cm long, belongs to a group of small trilobites called agnostids, which have only two or three trunk segments and a headshield and tailpiece of similar size and shape.

Task 2 Observations of fossil B

First examine fossil B with the naked eye, and then with your hand lens.

- Given that this organism is composed of many calcite plates, and is related to starfish and sea urchins, to which phylum does it belong?
- It belongs to the Phylum Echinodermata (Section 1.4 and Box 3.1).

Fossil B is a type of echinoderm called a crinoid ('cry-noyed'). Although crinoids occur today, they were far more common in the Palaeozoic and Mesozoic Eras. Most crinoids feed by bending their umbrella-like arrangement of flexible appendages (called '**arms**') downstream so as to catch a current, rather as in an umbrella being caught in the wind. Tube feet (the multipurpose tentacles; see Section 1.4) on the arms gather food particles suspended in the water, which are then wafted by small hair-like threads in grooves along the arms to the central mouth. Most ancient crinoids lived gregariously in shallow, current-swept areas, free of muddy sediment that would otherwise have tended to kill them by clogging their feeding mechanism.

Figure 3.8 A limestone of Carboniferous age composed of crinoid debris, especially stem plates. The stems are in varying degrees of disarticulation. Field of view 8 cm.

Most ancient crinoids, like fossil B, were attached to the sea floor by a stem or stalk with a root-like holdfast. The mouth and gut were situated in an enclosed cup at the top of the stem. In fossil B, the lower part of the stem is broken off. In life, the stem was fairly flexible, like the arms. The majority of living crinoids do not have a stem, and are capable of creeping around or even swimming. The few surviving stemmed forms generally live in deep water. Although they are animals, crinoids with stems look at first so like plants that they are often informally called 'sea lilies'. Shortly after death, the tiny organic fibres that alone hold the calcite plates together rot away, often causing the crinoid to disintegrate into separate plates that can be readily dispersed by currents or the movement of other organisms. In some ancient environments where crinoids were abundant, rocks have formed that are largely composed of isolated plates and stem fragments (Figure 3.8).

Crinoids have an arrangement of five '**rays**', each of which carries one or more arms that together form an efficient food-gathering structure. In fossil B, a number of arms are visible extending away from the central mouth area at the top of the stem. Attached to each arm are many fine side-branches called **pinnules**, each made of tiny plates, which are also part of the food-gathering apparatus. The pinnules can easily be seen in this specimen, especially in low-angle lighting.

- How many arms are visible in this replica?
- Parts of about 12 arms are visible.

Some arms are not visible, being on the underside of the original fossil. In this particular species, the number of arms per ray may vary, but it is typically four (giving a total of 20 arms).

- Are the plates of the stem, the cup and the arms all the same shape? (Use your hand lens.)
- No, the plates of these three areas are all different in shape.

Such differences in plate shape reflect detailed differences in the way the plates functioned.

- How would you describe the shape of the stem plates?
- They are disc- or coin-shaped. (There are basically two different sizes of disc-shaped plates, stacked alternately one upon the other, with some variation in size of the larger plates.)

Now complete the drawing of this fossil by filling in the two blank areas of the crinoid in Figure 3.9, i.e. part of the stem and an area of arms on the left side. Again, there is no need for any time-consuming shading etc; just use simple lines. Do not attempt to draw every plate on the arms — just draw a few of the larger ones near the arm base (see arms already drawn). Similarly, there is no need to draw every pinnule. Also make a quick drawing of the mound-shaped object to the left of the top of the crinoid stem — this is a different fossil, as we'll see shortly. Then label the following parts of the crinoid: *calcite stem plates*; *base of cup; base of a ray branching into four arms*; *arm*; *pinnules*; *central mouth area*. Draw a scale bar to show the extent of 1 cm.

To check your completed Figure 3.9, compare it with Figure 3.30 in the 'Comments on activities' section at the end of this book.

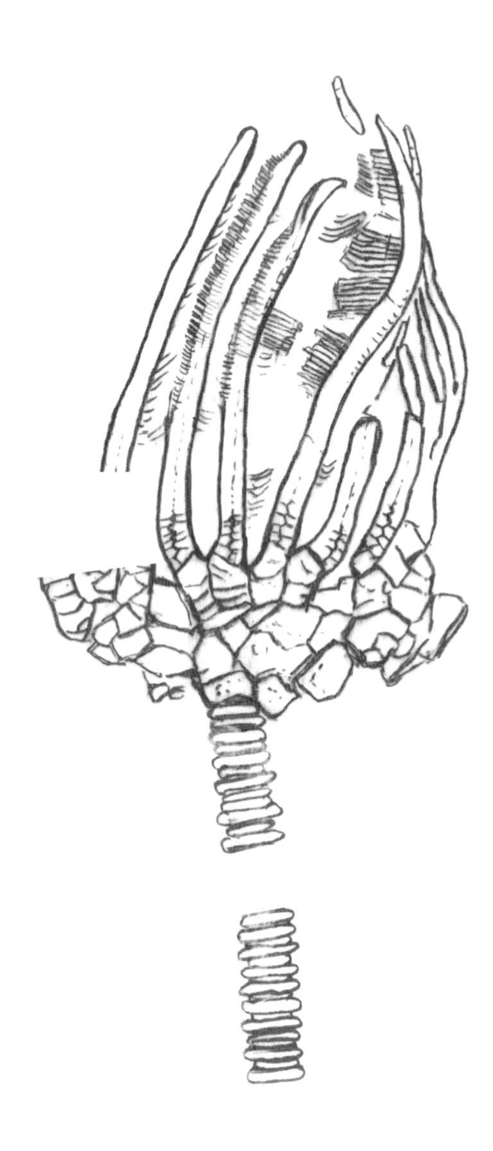

Figure 3.9 Partially completed illustration of fossil B, in plan view.

Question 3.2 Now let's briefly review what the study of fossils A and B has yielded about the environment in which the Wenlock Limestone was deposited. Both types of fossils are common in the Wenlock Limestone. In answering the following questions, you should state briefly the relevant evidence or reasoning, for each of your answers.

(a) Was it a marine or freshwater environment?

(b) What is likely to have been the water depth, in qualitative terms?

(c) Was the water normally clear or muddy?

(d) Given the answer to (c), how might this particular crinoid have died?

(e) Considering the state of preservation of these particular fossils, to what extent were the dead bodies of the trilobite and crinoid likely to have been subjected to persistent, strong currents? ◀

Corals

Corals are especially abundant in the Wenlock Limestone.

- According to Box 3.1, which two main groups of corals, each confined to the Palaeozoic Era, might you expect to find in the Silurian Period?
- Rugose corals and tabulate corals (Box 3.1).
- Which of these two coral groups only forms colonies?
- The tabulate corals are always colonial (whereas the rugose corals may be either colonial or solitary).

Figure 3.10 shows two rugose corals. When alive, the *Acervularia* colony in Figure 3.10a would probably have looked like a bunch of sea anemones, with each of them sitting in one of the bowl-shaped hollows of their calcite skeletons. The skeleton secreted by an individual, whether part of a colony or not, is called a **corallite**. In rugose corals, each corallite is usually divided by a series of conspicuous radial partitions, called **septa** (Figure 3.10). The corallites in a colony such as *Acervularia* share adjacent walls. In the centre of many corallites of *Acervularia* is a single, bowl-shaped hollow. Within some corallites there are one or more smaller hollows. These little hollows have the same basic arrangement of septa as in the larger corallites: they represent *new* individuals formed by the splitting up of their parent, enabling the coral colony to grow upward and outward by a process of asexual reproduction.

(a)

(b)

Figure 3.10 Rugose corals from the Wenlock Limestone. (a) *Acervularia ananas*, a rugose coral colony (5.5 cm); (b) *Kodonophyllum truncatum* (2.5 cm). This is a solitary individual from a species that more ofen forms colonies. Most other rugose coral species are either always solitary or always colonial.

(a)

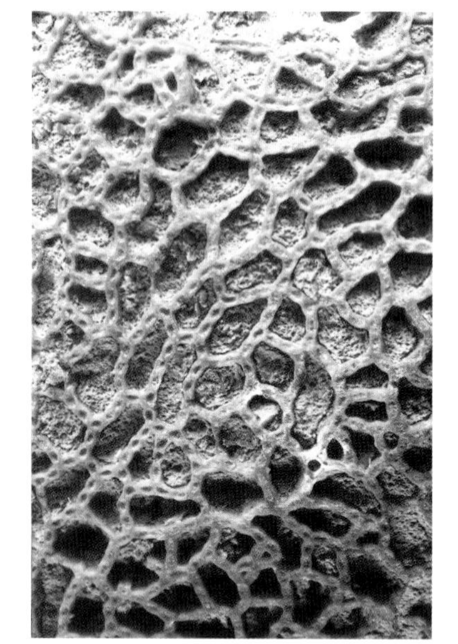

(b)

Figure 3.11 Tabulate corals from the Wenlock Limestone. (a) *Favosites* (field of view 8 cm); (b) *Halysites*, the 'chain coral' (field of view 3.5 cm).

Tabulate corals are distinguished by having much smaller corallites than those of rugose corals, and septa are either absent or short and inconspicuous. Tabulate coral colonies may take various forms, including massive (Figure 3.11a) or chains (Figure 3.11b).

The mound-shaped object you drew near the crinoid cup (fossil B) is actually a tabulate coral, *Favosites*; label it on Figure 3.9. Some Wenlock Limestone corals are also shown on pp.74 and 75 of the *Atlas;* see if you can distinguish the solitary corals from colonial ones. The coral at the bottom of the group on p.75 is a tabulate coral called *Heliolites*.

- What sort of environments do corals tend to be associated with today?
- Images of Australia's Great Barrier Reef and tropical islands like the Bahamas probably spring to mind (though not all corals live in shallow waters).
- According to Box 3.1, what is the main group of modern corals, and what is their age range?
- Scleractinian corals; Triassic to Recent.

Figure 3.12 shows some examples of modern coral skeletons, both solitary and colonial. Like rugose corals, scleractinians usually have conspicuous septa. However, unlike both rugose and tabulate corals, the skeleton of scleractinians is made of aragonite, not calcite. Although it is also a form of calcium carbonate, aragonite tends to alter to calcite or dissolve away, so that Mesozoic and Cenozoic corals (i.e. scleractinians) are often less well preserved than Palaeozoic ones.

Most, but not all, scleractinian corals today grow in warm, clear, shallow seas. The same seems to have been true of many ancient corals, including Palaeozoic ones. The requirement of many of today's corals for clear, shallow water is mostly because within the corals' soft tissues are tiny algae with which they live in an association of mutual benefit. The algae require clear, well-lit water for photosynthesis. By analogy with the preferences of most modern corals, and what is known of ancient ones, it

Figure 3.12 Examples of modern scleractinian coral skeletons. The largest is 9 cm across.

therefore seems very likely that the water of the Wenlock Limestone sea was warm rather than cold. This is supported by palaeomagnetic evidence (*Atlas*, p.169) showing that at this time Britain was about 25° south of the Equator (see the small map on top right of p.23 of the *Atlas*). Palaeozoic and scleractinian corals are, however, unrelated and there is evidence that Palaeozoic corals lacked a special association with algae.

Other Wenlock Limestone fossils

Among the other fossils common in the Wenlock Limestone are brachiopods (Figure 3.13a and b), gastropods (Figure 3.13c) and bryozoans (Figure 3.13d). You may need to reread Box 3.1 to remind yourself about various aspects of these groups.

The frontispiece is a reconstruction of a typical scene from a Wenlock Limestone environment. See if you can identify trilobites (alive, dead, or moulted pieces of exoskeleton), corals (colonies and isolated individuals), and crinoids among the various forms of life depicted. The cone-shaped squid-like animals are straight nautiloids (cephalopod molluscs, Box 3.1). ◀

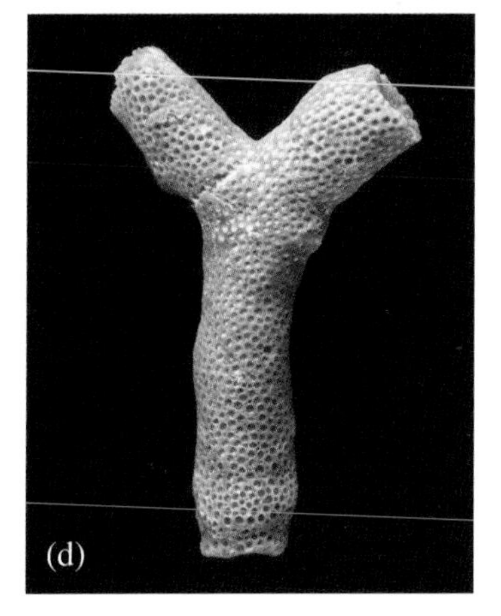

Figure 3.13 Some Wenlock Limestone fossils: (a) the brachiopod *Leptaena depressa* (2.5 cm); (b) the brachiopod *Atrypa reticularis* (2 cm); (c) the gastropod *Oriostoma* (4 cm); (d) the bryozoan *Hallopora elegantula* (2 cm).

3.5 The Devonian Period

Read the *Atlas*, pp.76–77. Do not worry too much about all the different names of fish groups in this, the 'Age of Fishes'.

Environmental change is known to have a significant impact on the evolution of life. For example, widening oceans generate barriers between populations and promote increasing genetic divergence between them over time. Narrowing oceans, rising mountain belts and the formation of large continental areas can also have major effects, causing both evolution and extinction. During the Silurian, the Iapetus Ocean had been narrowing (*Atlas*, p.72), allowing the progressive mixing of marine organisms that had previously been separated by a wide oceanic barrier. By the Devonian, the continental areas of Laurentia, Avalonia and Baltica had amalgamated to form a large land mass, with huge rivers and lakes that were colonized firstly by jawless fish and then by predatory jawed fish. (Jawed fish had first evolved in the Ordovician (*Atlas*, p.71), but only became abundant in the late Silurian and Devonian, evolving into many different marine and freshwater groups.) The rising mountain chains separated river systems and promoted the evolution of different species of fish in different inland waterways. Likewise, land plants were spreading globally, evolving distinct floras in particular regions with different climates.

We now look at one of the most significant developments in the evolution of our vertebrate ancestors — the first tetrapods (*Atlas G*, p.215) in the late Devonian.

3.6 Vertebrates move onto land

Read the *Atlas*, pp.78–79 and pp.82–83.

As we saw in Section 3.3, the move out of water on to land was a particularly difficult evolutionary transition, requiring many adaptations.

- What specific adaptations did vertebrates evolve for living on land, and why were they needed?

- Muscular limbs that lift the body and propel it forward, as movement on land could not easily be achieved with fish-like fins (note that limbless snakes today can move over land, though the skeletons of some snakes retain internal vestiges of limbs possessed by their ancestors); internal lungs, as the gills of fish collapse out of water; 'ears' to hear sound in air as opposed to water; and moist eyes and skin to prevent them drying up in air (*Atlas*, pp.78–79).

The earliest four-limbed vertebrates (i.e. **tetrapods**, *Atlas G*, p.215) are known from late Devonian river and lake deposits in Greenland. *Acanthostega* and *Ichthyostega* have a somewhat puzzling mixture of characteristics. They have four jointed, muscular limbs that were originally interpreted as legs for living on land, but they also have long, sideways-flattened, fish-type tails for swimming, a sensory system for detection of vibrations in water and, most important, fish-type gills. The current interpretation therefore sees the limbs as adaptations for life in a particular aquatic environment rather than for life on land. However, these limbs also had very appropriate preadaptations (Section 1.7) for the tetrapod descendants who did leave the water. By the early Carboniferous, limbs with five digits had become the norm, which has remained so ever since.

- Look at the panorama on pp.78–79 of the *Atlas*. How many digits ('fingers' or 'toes') did *Acanthostega* and *Ichthyostega* have on each limb?

- *Acanthostega* had eight digits, *Ichthyostega* had seven or possibly eight digits.

- What were the earliest tetrapod limbs supposedly used for in this late Devonian aquatic environment?

- The muscular limbs, hands and feet were used for additional propulsion (aiding the fish-like tail), for holding on to plants and perhaps digging for shellfish (*Atlas*, p.78).

By early Carboniferous times, fossils from localities such as East Kirkton in Scotland reveal the existence of several different tetrapod groups (*Atlas*, pp.82–83). Some of these were still fully aquatic, but others, such as the superficially lizard-like *Westlothiana* and the salamander-like *Balanerpeton*, had probably made the transition to a semi-aquatic life. Life in the water was hazardous, with intense competition for food, and part of the incentive for early tetrapods to leave the water may have been to exploit abundant food resources on land. However, life on land could also be dangerous, as witnessed, for example, by the scorpion, *Pulmonoscorpius*, which grew up to 70 cm long.

You might wonder why the word 'tetrapod' is used here instead of amphibian or reptile. Certainly, modern tetrapods are clearly separated into amphibians, reptiles, birds and mammals, largely on the basis of their distinctive reproductive systems. Amphibians breed in water, where they lay unprotected eggs which are externally fertilized. By contrast, reptiles, birds and mammals use internal fertilization. In reptiles and birds, the embryo develops in fluid surrounded by a protective shell — an egg that can be laid on land. In nearly all mammals, the developing embryo is also surrounded by fluid and a protective membrane, but is retained in the mother's body for some time before birth. Such protective membranes are not confined to the mammals but are also found in reptiles and birds, all of which are grouped as **amniotes** (see *Atlas G*, p.204). The amniotes are therefore more independent of water than amphibians whose embryos are not protected by such membranes and therefore have to develop in water. The problem is that the early tetrapod fossils do not preserve direct evidence of reproductive habits. Also, during early tetrapod evolution there would not have been so clear a separation between amphibians and reptiles as we find today. Only later, when clearly identifiable amphibian or reptilian characteristics emerge in the fossils, is classification easier.

As we shall see shortly, by Carboniferous times terrestrial food chains were already well developed with a great variety of plants such as tree-sized clubmosses, seed plants and tree ferns and smaller, ground-covering ferns. These plants supported a wide variety of invertebrate life, including many arthropods, which provided abundant food for the carnivorous land-living tetrapods.

3.6.1 An outline of vertebrate evolution

Let's now place the early evolution of tetrapods in perspective by taking an overview of the whole of vertebrate evolution.

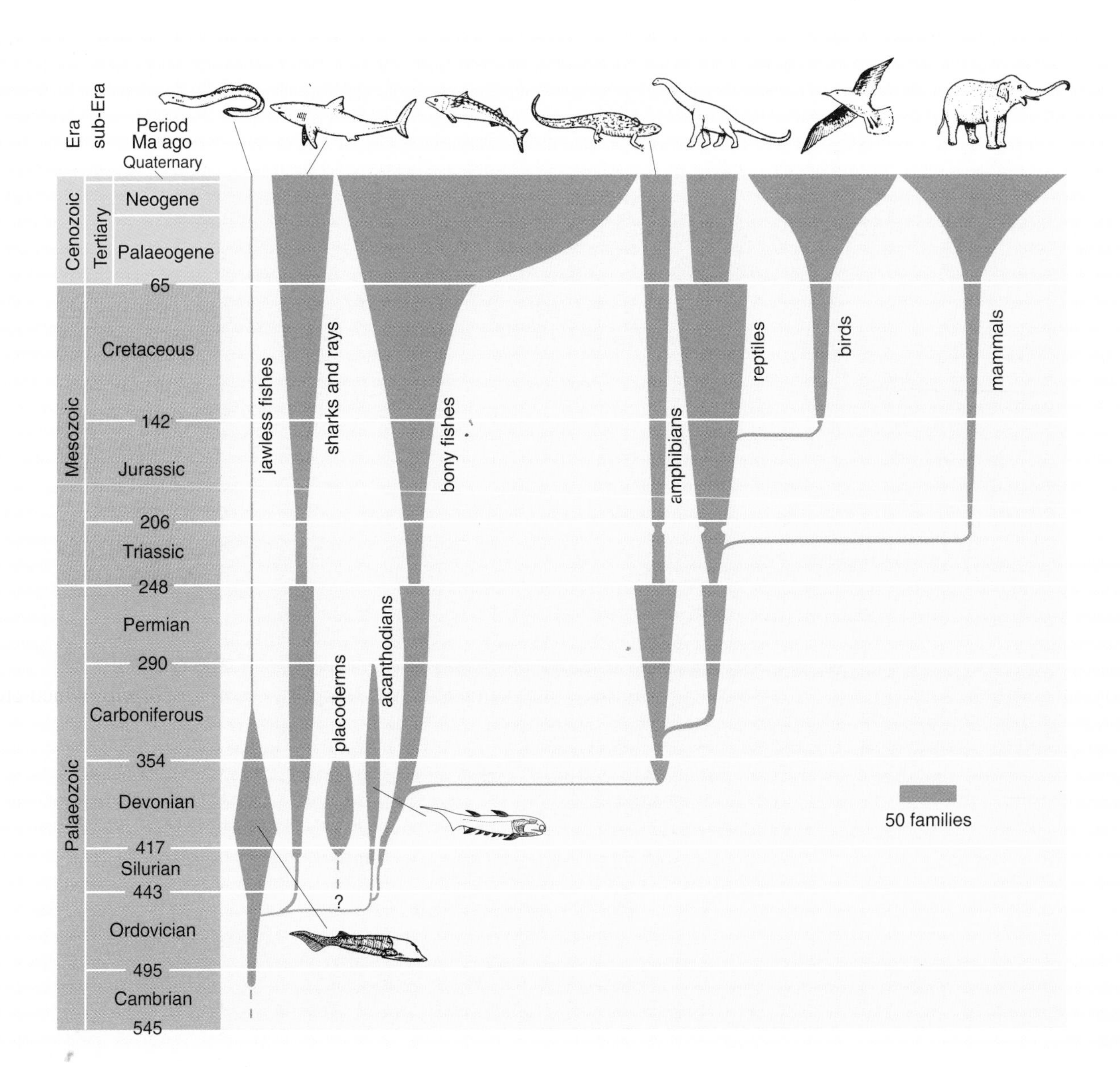

Figure 3.14 Geological ranges of vertebrates showing when various groups evolved from each other during the Phanerozoic. The width of each group indicates its approximate diversity (as number of families); note the scale bar. The wide horizontal separation of some newly evolved groups from their ancestors (e.g. mammals from reptiles) does *not* indicate huge, abrupt change but is simply a consequence of the way the diagram is drawn.

Given the ubiquity of our own primate (*Atlas G*, p.213) species, and familiarity with domesticated animals such as cats, dogs, and rabbits, our view of the relative diversity and abundance of the main vertebrate groups tends to be biased towards mammals. However, a tally of living vertebrate species reminds us that mammals are not as dominant as some might imagine. In round terms, the total number of living vertebrate species is over 46 000 (which compares, for example, with some 110 000 species of molluscs and more than 80 000 species of roundworms (nematodes)). Living mammals and amphibians each number around 4300 species, whereas there are some 6500 reptile species, 9100 bird species and over 21 000 species of bony fish, and about 800 species of sharks and rays, the cartilaginous fish.

- Which of today's five vertebrate classes (Box 3.1) were in existence by the end of the Triassic Period (see Figure 3.14)? (If you're not sure where classes fit in the taxonomic hierarchy, look again at Table 1.1.)

- Fishes, amphibians, reptiles and mammals had all evolved by then, about 206 Ma ago.

- In terms of families, which living vertebrate groups shown in Figure 3.14 are at their highest diversity today? Which living groups were more diverse in the past, and when was their peak of diversity?

- Sharks and rays, bony fishes, birds and mammals are at their maximum family diversity today. Jawless fish were most diverse in the Devonian; amphibians in the Permian; and reptiles in the Cretaceous.

In discussions such as this, it is important to be aware which taxonomic category (Section 1.3) is being considered because the picture can change if other measures of diversity (e.g. species) are used.

Question 3.3 From Figure 3.14, estimate roughly (to the nearest five) the number of living families of reptiles and of mammals. Then, using the data on species numbers given above, work out which of these two groups has, on average, more species per family. ◀

As we have already seen, the vertebrates were initially slow to diversify. From their Cambrian start, it was not until late Ordovician times that the early jawed fish evolved into different groups, though some were subsequently to become extinct (the placoderms, see *Atlas*, pp.76–77, and acanthodians, see *Atlas*, p.83). From Figure 3.14 it becomes clear why the Devonian is often called the 'Age of Fishes': not only was there a greater diversity of fish groups than at any other time but most of the other vertebrate classes had yet to evolve.

Figure 3.14 reveals a variety of patterns in fish evolution, including some major setbacks. The placoderms became extinct at the end of the Devonian, coincident with a decrease in early tetrapod diversity. Sharks, rays and bony fishes suffered a major extinction at the end of the Permian, coincident with a similar setback for amphibians and reptiles, part of a mass extinction event as we shall see (Section 3.10). Today, the total number of fish families is at its highest ever, mainly due to the bony fishes.

- When did the total number of bony fish families begin to increase steeply from some 95 families to their present total of about 260?

- In early Tertiary (Palaeogene) times.

Let's now look at the history of tetrapods. After emerging in late Devonian times, tetrapod communities were initially dominated by amphibians, especially in Carboniferous and Permian times, when a wide variety of amphibian groups evolved and died out. Amphibians remained large during the Palaeozoic Era, often 1–2 m long — huge by the standards of today's frogs, toads and newts, which have a relatively recent, Mesozoic origin. The first reptiles appeared in the early Carboniferous.

- What crucial adaptation did reptiles evolve that freed them from the amphibian dependence on being near water to lay eggs and develop tadpoles?

- A shelled egg that did not dry out in air (the amniotic egg) (Section 3.6).

At first the earliest Carboniferous reptiles were quite small, superficially lizard-like predators (see *Atlas* pp.84–85). They lived mostly on arthropods, such as dragonflies and cockroaches, in the dense equatorial Carboniferous forests and swamps (Section 3.8). The energy of sunlight trapped during photosynthesis became stored in vast amounts of plant litter that accumulated on the floor of the forests and in swamps. Eventually, this debris was buried, compressed and converted by heat and pressure into coal; 300 Ma later the energy from Carboniferous sunlight fuelled the Industrial Revolution.

Not until Permian times did reptiles begin to diversify widely and increase in size; some even returned to living in the sea. Others evolved certain mammal-like features, such as the beginnings of tooth differentiation. This allowed for separate functions such as large dagger-shaped teeth for defence and killing prey, and smaller cheek teeth for efficient processing of food before digestion. One of these groups that survived the end Permian mass extinction eventually evolved into the first mammals in the late Triassic (Section 4.4).

Question 3.4 Using Figure 3.14, measure the approximate number of families (to the nearest five) present in the four main vertebrate groups (sharks and rays, bony fishes, amphibians and reptiles), first at the end of the Permian and then in the early Triassic. From these totals, calculate the percentage change in family diversity. ◀

After the end Permian extinction event, the reptiles recovered and gradually became the dominant group by the end of Triassic times, though both reptiles and amphibians were set back by another, late Triassic, extinction event.

- Which group do you think was mainly responsible for the dominance of reptiles in the Mesozoic?

- It was, of course, the dinosaurs, though dinosaurs were only one of many kinds of Mesozoic reptiles.

Dinosaurs were a special group of reptiles — special not least because, after their origin in the late Triassic, they became the dominant land animals for over 150 Ma. They filled almost every niche possible for large land vertebrates. They included carnivores, herbivores and a few omnivores (mixed diet), and ranged in size from that of a chicken to vast plant eaters, such as the *Brachiosaurus*, which grew up to 25 m long and weighed up to 40 tonnes. Dinosaurs never, however, took to the air or to the oceans: other large reptiles — the pterosaurs (*Atlas G*, p.213) — dominated the skies, and marine reptiles such as ichthyosaurs (p.210), plesiosaurs (p.213) and mosasaurs (p.211) flourished in the sea. The major surviving groups of reptiles, the crocodiles (p.207), turtles and tortoises, lizards and snakes also all appeared in Mesozoic times. Much evidence suggests that birds evolved from dinosaurs in late Jurassic times.

The great success of the Mesozoic reptiles came to a dramatic halt at the end of the Cretaceous (Sections 3.10 and 4.11). Reptile diversity was cut back from about 60 families to 30 and never fully recovered (Figure 3.14). The bony fishes rapidly increased in diversity in the early Tertiary.

For a long time after their late Triassic origin, mammals remained small, perhaps nocturnal, shrew-like creatures living in the nooks and crannies of the dinosaur world. But once the large Mesozoic reptiles had become extinct, mammals were able to diversify into the wide range of niches that became vacant (Section 5.2). Plants, which also suffered some extinctions at the end of the Cretaceous, continued to have a role in the evolution of both vertebrates and invertebrates. The rise of flowering plants (angiosperms, *Atlas G*, p.204; Section 4.9) and pollinating insects, together with climate change in the early Tertiary, promoted the evolution of grasses (*Atlas G*, p.209), which in turn supported the spectacular rise of grazing mammals. As we'll see in Section 5, it was perhaps the climate-driven change in vegetation that promoted our own evolution from tree-dwelling primates (*Atlas G*, p.213) in late Cenozoic times. Global cooling as part of the initial descent into the Quaternary Ice Age caused retreat and fragmentation of the extensive forests of central Africa and their replacement by more open grasslands. This gave an adaptive advantage to a group of more upright-walking primates — the hominids (*Atlas G*, p.209). Our own species, *Homo sapiens*, appeared only 100 000 to 400 000 years ago (depending on how the origin of the species is defined).

3.7 An outline of plant evolution

Read the *Atlas*, p.136, up to the section entitled 'Flowering plants', which will introduce you to the overall pattern of land plant evolution.

Some of the plant types mentioned in the *Atlas* are probably new to you. Figure 3.15 is a simple 'balloon' diagram that shows the major plant groups, past and present. This is similar to diagrams such as Figure 3.14. The point at which each balloon begins marks the first fossil evidence of the group and the end of the balloon indicates the group's extinction. The width of the balloon gives a qualitative impression of how 'important' the group was at any given time, where importance is a combination of both species diversity and abundance (based on numbers of individuals and their estimated biomass, i.e. mass of living material). This, of course, is a very imprecise measure but it provides us with an insight into ancient plant life.

The earliest land plants

The earliest land plants were probably no more advanced than simple algae that formed crusts around the margins of water bodies. They may have existed as long ago as the late Precambrian. As was mentioned in Section 3.2, by the Ordovician, there is evidence that plant life on land may have reached the levels of complexity seen in simple bryophytes (*Atlas*, p.136 and *Atlas G*, p.205) or fungi. Evidence for this is not in the form of fossils of complete plants but isolated spores and tube-shaped cells. These earliest land plants had adaptations for dispersal of spores by either water or air. Tissues dedicated to the transport of fluids around the plant body had evolved. These plants were still very small, but they started the greening of the land.

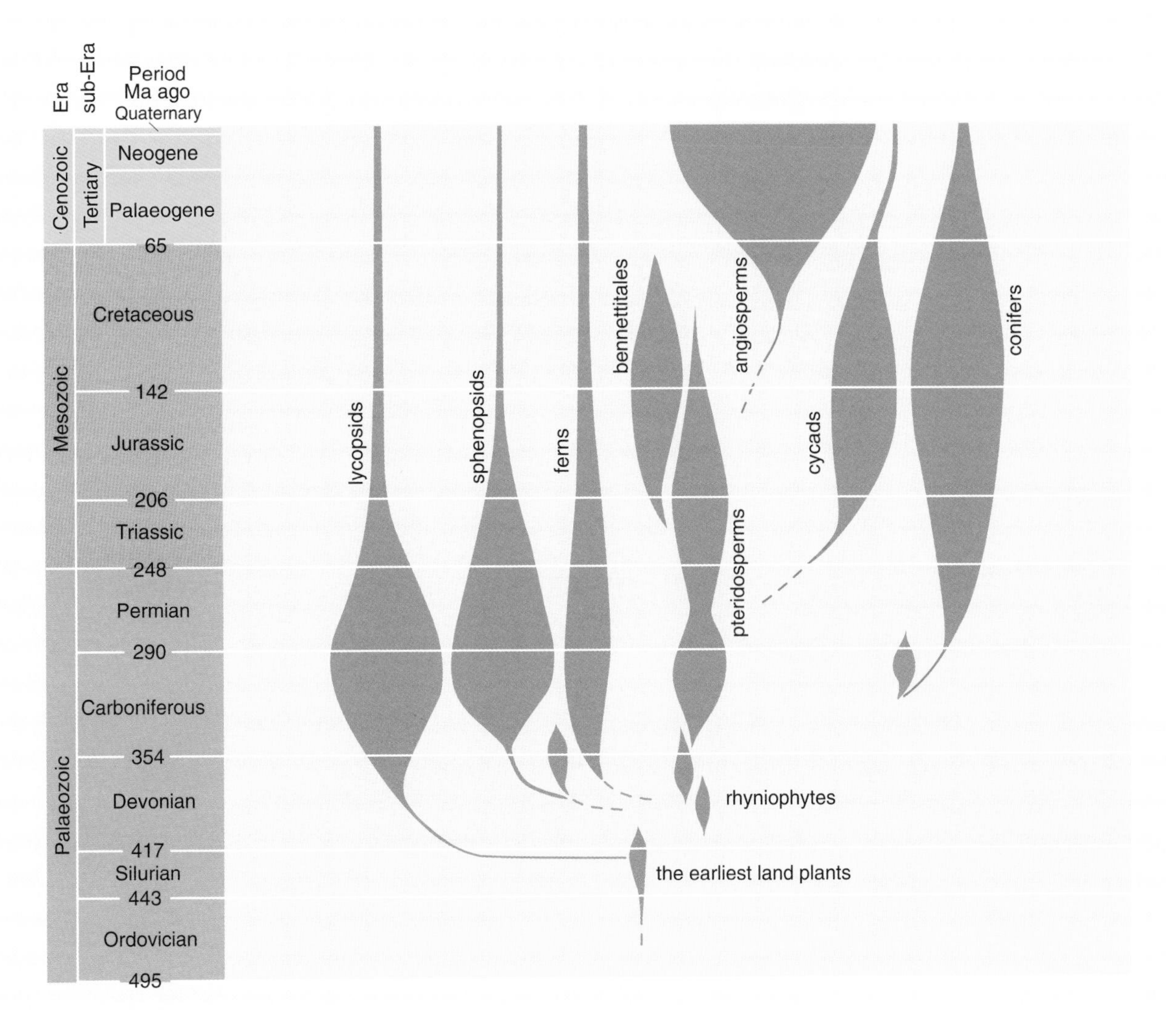

Figure 3.15 The time ranges and evolutionary connections (where known) of the major plant groups.

One of the first well-known land plants is *Cooksonia*, which we met before in Section 3.3, Figure 3.3a (a fossil specimen), and p.75 of the *Atlas* (reconstruction). It had specialized cells for carrying fluids around the plant that were strong enough to enable upright growth; it was thus a vascular land plant (*Atlas G*, p.215). This plant is believed to have been no more than a few cm tall, although its base has not been found. All that remains of *Cooksonia* are the small, simply branched stalks that have, at their tips, spore-bearing pouches called **sporangia**. The reason we find only these parts of the plant is because they alone were covered with a **cuticle**. This cuticle limited the amount of water that was lost by the plant to the atmosphere, but it was also very resistant to decay and so survived in the fossil record. Spores also have a waterproof jacket made of an even more decay-resistant substance, so these too often survive hundreds of millions of years entombed in rock. The basal parts of the plant did not need a cuticle covering because they were in contact with the moist surface of the ground. Modern plants still possess cuticles and these often have the additional protection of a waxy coating — like that on an apple.

By the early and middle Devonian, land plants were becoming more complex and growing taller.

- Why might selection have favoured plants that grew taller?
- Taller plants are more likely to succeed in competition for light and the dispersal of potential progeny is helped by being high up off the ground.

One of the best insights into late early-Devonian plant communities comes from a deposit called the Rhynie chert at Rhynie in Aberdeenshire, Scotland (*Atlas*, p.136). Here, mineral-rich hot springs periodically inundated a nearby marsh community, preserving the plants in great detail. Not only have the cell walls been replaced by silica (quartz in a form called chert) but the spaces in porous tissues have also been filled in by silica.

- What is the name given to the type of preservation in which spaces are filled by additional minerals?
- Permineralization (Section 1.2).

Rhynia gwynne-vaughanii was a leafless plant with simple branches and sporangia at the branch tips. Internally the plant was also simple, with a single strand of fluid-transporting cells, a mass of packing cells and, on the outside, a layer of 'skin' cells, covered by a cuticle (Figure 3.16). It was a rhyniophyte, a group which contained the forerunners of most other groups of land plants (Figure 3.15).

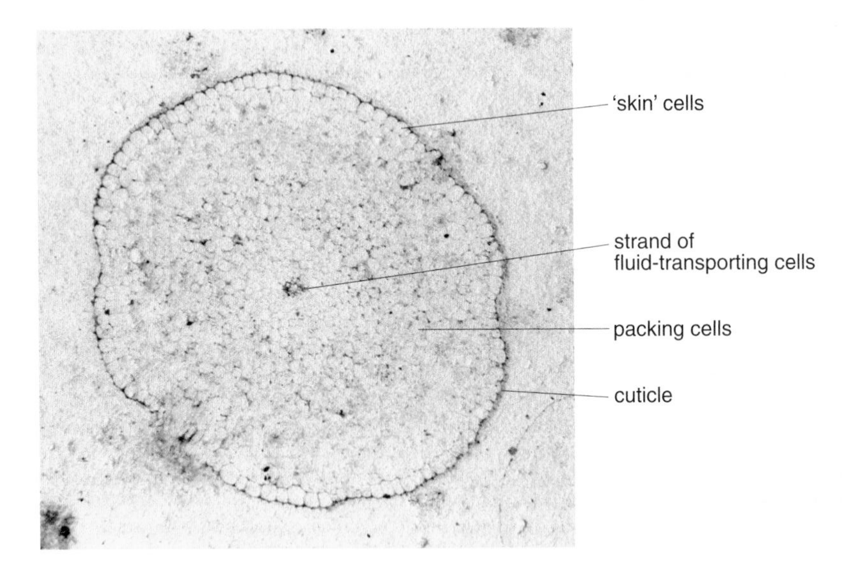

Figure 3.16 A cross-section through the stem of *Rhynia gwynne-vaughanii*, a Devonian rhyniophyte from Rhynie in Scotland. The stem diameter is 2.5 mm.

By middle Devonian times, plants were reaching a metre or so in height. Instead of just simple branching there was a main stem and side branches, and the surfaces of the plants were covered with spines that may have helped in mutual support. Sporangia were borne in large clusters, as shown in Figure 3.17.

By the end of the Devonian, the first trees with woody trunks had evolved. Look again at the reconstruction of late Devonian life on pp.78–79 of the *Atlas*. Some of the trees seem to be rather like conifers, but instead of needles their leaves resembled fern fronds and they reproduced, not by seeds like conifers, but by spores, like ferns. These plants are members of an extinct group called the **progymnosperms**. The generic name for their foliage, which in turn gives its name to the reconstructed tree, is *Archaeopteris*.

(a)

(b)

Figure 3.17 (a) A Devonian plant, *Psilophyton*, extracted by dissolving the surrounding rock in acid. Out of a basal mass of stems that grew along the ground (termed rhizomes) rose an erect stem covered with spines. At the end of the stem was a series of small branches terminating in clusters of spore-bearing sporangia, shown in greater detail in (b), another specimen. Length of specimen in (a) 12 cm and in (b) 6.5 cm.

- Which 'balloon' in Figure 3.15 do you think represents the progymnosperms?
- It is the small one that sits on the 354 Ma time line between the ferns and sphenopsids. Note that there is no direct connection to any other plant group, reflecting uncertainty about its ancestors and descendants.

Lycopsids (clubmosses)

Cooksonia was not the only Silurian plant. Some Silurian plant fossils from Australia are quite large and belong to a group of plants, the lycopsids, that included forms whose descendants would eventually dominate the Carboniferous coal forests. *Baragwanathia* (Figure 3.18), like almost all plants in this group, had helically arranged, simple strap-like 'leaves' around a creeping and partly upright stem. The term 'leaves' is put in quotes because these structures are not true leaves in the sense of those that we are most familiar with today. They were simple outgrowths of the stem, whereas modern leaves are branching systems webbed with photosynthetic tissue. These stem outgrowths of *Baragwanathia* are called **microphylls** (scale leaves) to distinguish them from true leaves. A characteristic of all lycopsids is that they reproduced by means of spores produced in kidney-shaped sporangia attached to the upper side of the helically arranged microphylls along the sides of the stem.

Figure 3.18 *Baragwanathia*, a lycopsid, from Silurian rocks in Australia. A penknife gives an indication of scale.

You can see from Figure 3.15 that the lycopsids began to diversify in the late Devonian and by the late Carboniferous they dominated much of the world's vegetation. Note that another term for lycopsids is clubmosses (*Atlas G*, p.206), but this can be misleading because some ancient clubmosses were huge trees, very different from the 'mosses' encountered today. We will return to lycopsids when looking at Carboniferous swamp forests in Section 3.8.

Sphenopsids (horsetails)

Sphenopsids or horsetails (*Atlas G*, p.209) are another group that played a major role in the Carboniferous. The only modern representatives are the 'horsetails' or 'scouring rushes' which total about 20 species, all in the genus *Equisetum*

(a)

(b)

Figure 3.19 Living and fossil sphenopsids. (a) *Equisetum*, a modern sphenopsid (horsetail). Field of view about 25 cm. Note the whorls of branches arranged at intervals along the stem, a characteristic of sphenopsids. This feature can also be seen in (b), a branch of *Calamites*, a Carboniferous sphenopsid (field of view 30 cm).

(Figure 3.19a). Today these plants are rarely more than a few metres tall, but in the Carboniferous their ancestors, called *Calamites* (Figure 3.19b), grew to around 20 m in height. A piece of fossil *Calamites* foliage is shown on p.84 of the *Atlas*. This foliage has the separate generic name *Annularia* and it is a common fossil in the mudstones associated with British coal-bearing strata. *Calamites* tended to grow near rivers, but other, smaller sphenopsids grew in the swamps. All sphenopsids, past and present, reproduce by means of spores.

Ferns

The ferns (*Atlas G*, p.208) have a long evolutionary history stretching back into the late Devonian (Figure 3.15). They all reproduce by means of spores which are usually (but not always) borne in sporangia situated in clusters on the underside of fronds. You can readily recognize these clusters when they are ripe, as they become dark and look like spots or bars on the undersides of fern leaves. Ferns come in a variety of shapes and sizes; some have a small stem or rhizome that sits on or under the soil surface, while some so-called tree ferns (*Atlas G*, p.215), produce a trunk made up of roots and stems intertwined. Some have extremely elongated fronds that scramble over and climb up other plants, while some are aquatic and float on the surface of ponds and lakes. The tree habit dates back to the late Devonian but has evolved many times in different lineages of ferns. The Cretaceous tree fern *Tempskya* is shown on p.111 of the *Atlas*, and a modern tree fern can be seen on p.82.

Seed ferns (pteridosperms)

There are many fern and fern-like fossils in Carboniferous rocks. Sometimes it is very difficult to distinguish true ferns from seed ferns just from the foliage. The difference, as the name suggests, is that seed ferns (*Atlas G*, p.214), otherwise known as pteridosperms, reproduced by seeds and not spores. Unlike a spore, a **seed** has an outer protective covering that is derived, in evolutionary terms, from highly modified branches. Another difference is that, unlike all except the largest spores, seeds have their own food supply. All the plant groups we considered before seed ferns reproduced by spores, but from now on in this section we will be considering **seed plants** (*Atlas G*, p.214). Until we get to the angiosperms (flowering plants), all the seed plants we will be looking at are termed **gymnosperms** (*Atlas G*, p.209). The term ‘gymnosperm’ literally means ‘naked seed’ and they are given this name because their seeds are not enclosed in an outer covering.

Seed ferns were particularly abundant in the late Carboniferous and in the Triassic and Jurassic, but during the Cretaceous they succumbed to competition from the angiosperms and eventually became extinct before the end of the Cretaceous (Figure 3.15). There were many different families of seed ferns. *Medullosa* looked like a tree fern (see the reconstruction on p.85 of the *Atlas*), while others such as the glossopterids of Gondwana (*Atlas*, pp.87, 88 and *Atlas G*, p.209) looked like true trees and bushes. The significance of the seed ferns cannot be overestimated because it is from this group that cycads and bennettitales arose, and directly or indirectly, the angiosperms too.

Cycads

As you can see from Figure 3.15, the cycads (*Atlas G*, p.207) are a group that has survived to the present day from at least Permian times, and they may even have originated in the Carboniferous. Cycads reproduce by means of seeds, mostly borne on modified fronds grouped together to form cones. The only living exception is the most primitive living example, *Cycas*, where modified fronds bearing seeds are separate from one another and do not form a cone. Plants are either female or male, the male plants always producing pollen from cones. (In general terms a **cone** is a specialized branch with clusters of overlapping, scale-like modified leaves that bear the reproductive organs.) Modern cycads typically have a squat trunk bearing whorls of leathery, evergreen fronds (Figure 3.20a). They are found only in regions where frosts are absent or not severe, and each genus occurs on several different continents. This fragmented distribution indicates that the modern plants are the remnants of a previously more widespread distribution. This is confirmed by fossil evidence that shows that the group was distributed worldwide in the Mesozoic, and even made up a significant component of polar vegetation when there were no ice caps. Unlike their modern counterparts, however, these polar cycads were deciduous and had vine-like stems.

Bennettitales

This group of cycad-like plants was restricted to the Mesozoic. Members of the bennettitales produced seeds in cone-like structures, which were sometimes surrounded by protective scales or **bracts**. Male and female plants were sometimes separate, but they could also be bisexual and the reproductive structures sometimes even had both male and female parts arranged in a similar way to that in flowering

Figure 3.20 Cycads. (a) Modern cycads, of the genus *Cycas*. (b) A fossil cycad leaf. Length 70 cm.

Figure 3.21 A reproductive structure of the bennettite *Williamsonia pacifica*, Cretaceous (diameter 22 cm).

plants. Figure 3.21 shows a picture of a bennettite reproductive structure. Such fossils have been found in cliffs along the Yorkshire coast. The fossil leaves of cycads and bennettites are often very difficult to tell apart. Distinctions are usually made on the basis of microscopic details of the cell walls recorded in the cuticle.

Conifers

- When did conifers originate?
- In the late Carboniferous (Figure 3.15).

Conifers (*Atlas G*, p.206) rose to dominate many plant communities in the Mesozoic, and are, of course, still a highly successful group, thriving especially in the great forests across North America and Eurasia. Most conifers are woody trees which reproduce by means of seeds borne in cones. The single-sex cones (i.e. either male or female) are usually on the same plant but sometimes they are on separate plants. In some conifers, such as juniper, the cones have been modified to be fleshy, attractive berry-like structures.

Figure 3.22 The female cones of a Douglas Fir. The seeds of conifers such as this are situated between the cone scales and the more central part of the cone. The tongue-like bracts (visibly protruding in this species) lie on the outer side of the cone scales.

- Why might selection have favoured the evolution of attractive-looking, fleshy berries?
- The more likely that animals are to eat the berries, the more widely dispersed will be the seeds they contain. The animals get the benefit of the fleshy food, and the seeds are passed out in the animals' droppings, along with a dose of natural fertilizer to start them off. This is just one of many examples of **coevolution** between plants and animals, in which reciprocal adaptations have been produced in two or more species by prolonged, close interaction.

A typical conifer female cone has seeds borne on a woody scale associated with a tongue-like bract. These bracts can be seen protruding from the Douglas Fir cone pictured in Figure 3.22, but in many other conifers, such as the pines, the bracts are small and cannot be seen without taking the cones apart. Pollen is produced in a male cone which is smaller and much less conspicuous than a mature female cone.

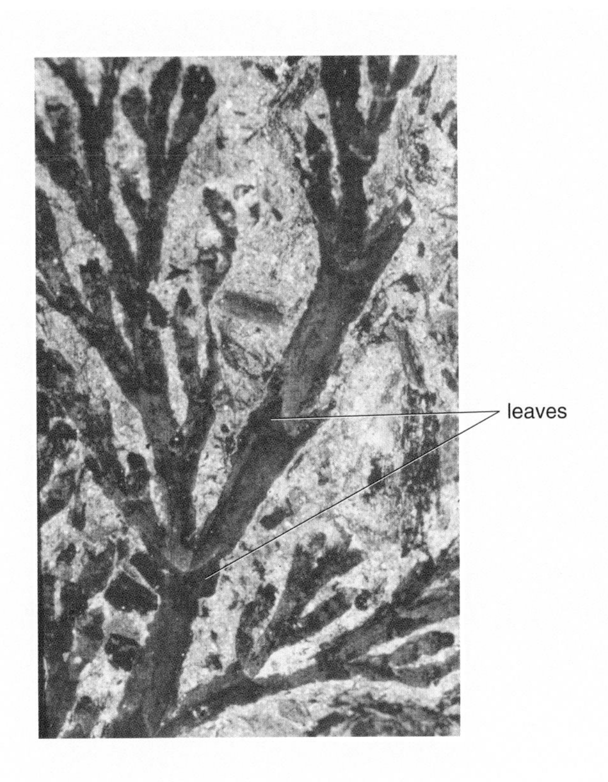

(a)

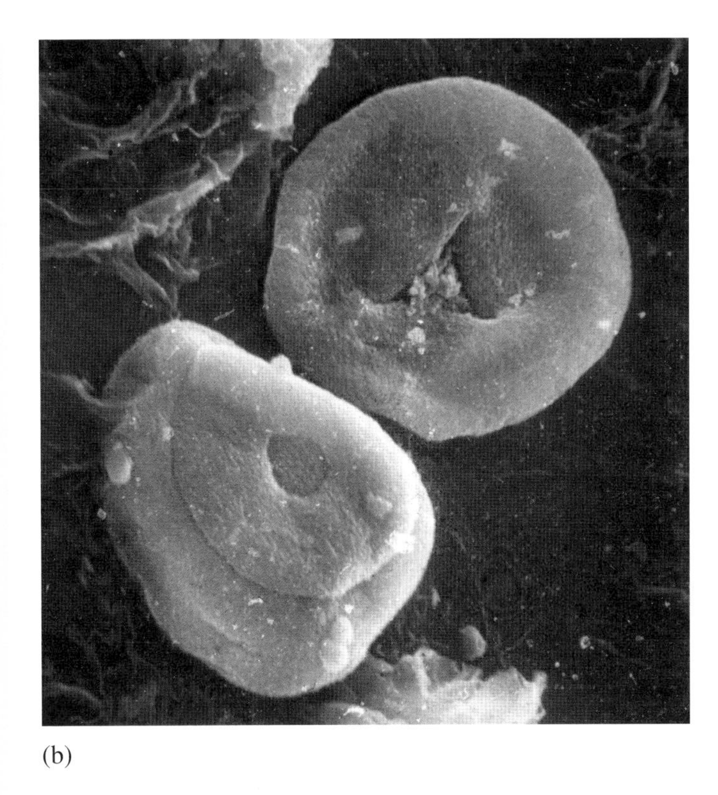

(b)

Figure 3.23 Fossils of Cretaceous cheirolepidiaceous conifers. (a) A branch of *Frenelopsis*. Note the whorls of small leaves around the stems. The width of the thickest stem here is about 2 mm; (b) pollen grains, about 0.05 mm in diameter. On one side of each grain there is a pore (visible in the lower left grain), whilst on the other side there is a triangular mark (upper right grain).

Most modern families of conifers arose in the Mesozoic but one abundant conifer family that disappeared at the end of the Cretaceous was the Cheirolepidiaceae (Figure 3.23). These dominated the vegetation at low latitudes (below 40°). They were adapted to seasonal drought. They had very thick cuticles, small leaves, and were deciduous, dropping their photosynthetic shoots when conditions became too dry. You can find abundant fossils of cheirolepidiaceous conifers in the early Cretaceous strata of southern England.

Conifer wood is quite common in the fossil record. Figure 3.24 shows a cross-section through a 95 Ma old conifer tree trunk. Note that all the cells appear to be rather similar, although those produced near a ring boundary get smaller as the tree enters dormancy. Examination of fossil tree rings can provide useful data on past climates, particularly as each cell usually represents less than a week's growth.

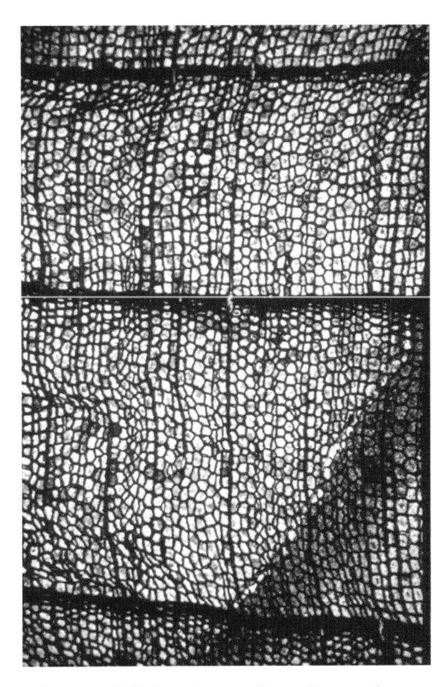

Figure 3.24 A section through fossil conifer wood. The sample was prepared by grinding the fossil so thin (about 0.05 mm) that light can pass through it, as here. The direction of growth is from bottom to top. Three ring boundaries can be seen where the tree stopped growing during winter.

Ginkgos

The maidenhair tree, *Ginkgo biloba*, is the only living species of a group that was highly diverse and widespread in the Mesozoic, and is often considered a 'living fossil'. The ancestors and closest relatives of ginkgos (*Atlas G.* p.209) are uncertain. Ginkgos (or ginkophytes as the *Atlas* sometimes calls them) are not shown separately in Figure 3.15.

The last major group of land plants to evolve was the flowering plants (angiosperms) (Figure 3.15). They became a significant part of global vegetation in the middle and late Cretaceous, and are the most economically important group of plants today. We will consider angiosperms in more detail in Section 4.9.

3.8 The Carboniferous coal forests

For anyone living in Britain the Carboniferous was one of the most significant periods in Earth's history. It was during the Carboniferous that vast amounts of peat were formed — peat that eventually, over time and with heat and pressure deep in the Earth, was converted to coal. This coal was the fuel for the Industrial Revolution and the foundation for Britain's economic strength. The economic importance of Carboniferous coal was not restricted to the United Kingdom. Carboniferous coal is found throughout North America and Europe. To understand some of the reasons why such a large amount of plant material was buried at that time we first have to look at the plants which made up the forests.

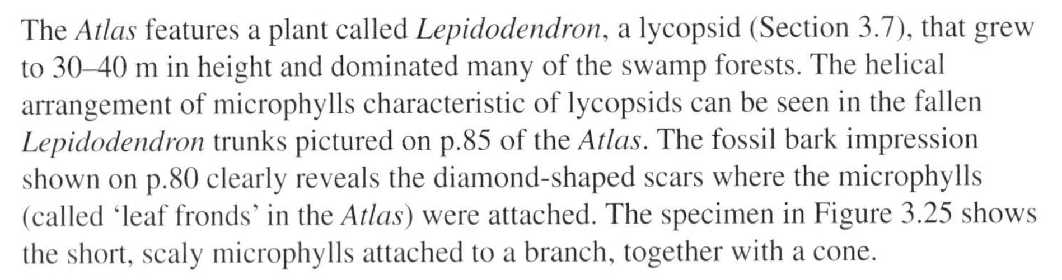

Read the *Atlas*, pp.80–81 and pp.84–85.

Figure 3.25 A branch of *Lepidodendron* with a cone. Field of view is 50 cm.

The *Atlas* features a plant called *Lepidodendron*, a lycopsid (Section 3.7), that grew to 30–40 m in height and dominated many of the swamp forests. The helical arrangement of microphylls characteristic of lycopsids can be seen in the fallen *Lepidodendron* trunks pictured on p.85 of the *Atlas*. The fossil bark impression shown on p.80 clearly reveals the diamond-shaped scars where the microphylls (called 'leaf fronds' in the *Atlas*) were attached. The specimen in Figure 3.25 shows the short, scaly microphylls attached to a branch, together with a cone.

Lepidodendron had a very simple branching pattern in which two equal-sized branches arose from each branch point. This equal branching pattern can just about be seen in the reconstructions of living *Lepidodendron* trees on p.84 of the *Atlas*. The roots also had this branching pattern, which is clearly visible in the fossil roots shown on p.81 of the *Atlas*. This simple division is quite unlike the branching pattern in other trees where the branches are unequal. It is, however, a feature of many primitive plants and is retained in modern, very much smaller lycopsids such as the clubmosses *Lycopodium* and *Selaginella*.

We saw in Section 1.3 that plants are very rarely preserved as whole fossils but normally occur as isolated individual parts, such as leaves, cones, roots, trunks, etc. Because these different parts are found separately in the rock record, and are discovered at different times before a whole plant can be reconstructed, each plant *part* tends to get a different Latin binomial name (Section 1.3). So when the whole plant is eventually reconstructed it is made up of different plant parts, each one of which may have its own genus and species name, although all the parts belong, of course, to a single biological species. You can see a good example of this in Figure 3.26. The whole *Lepidodendron* tree gets its name from the name originally given to the parts of the trunk and branches with characteristic diamond-shaped markings where the microphylls, *Lepidophylloides*, were attached. Lower down the trunk these markings are not obvious and this part has the name *Knorria*. The male cones are called *Lepidostrobus* and they contain spores called *Lycospora*. Other parts are as labelled in Figure 3.26. The rooting systems, called *Stigmaria* (see *Atlas*, p.81), were covered in rootlets arranged, like the leaves, in a helical pattern.

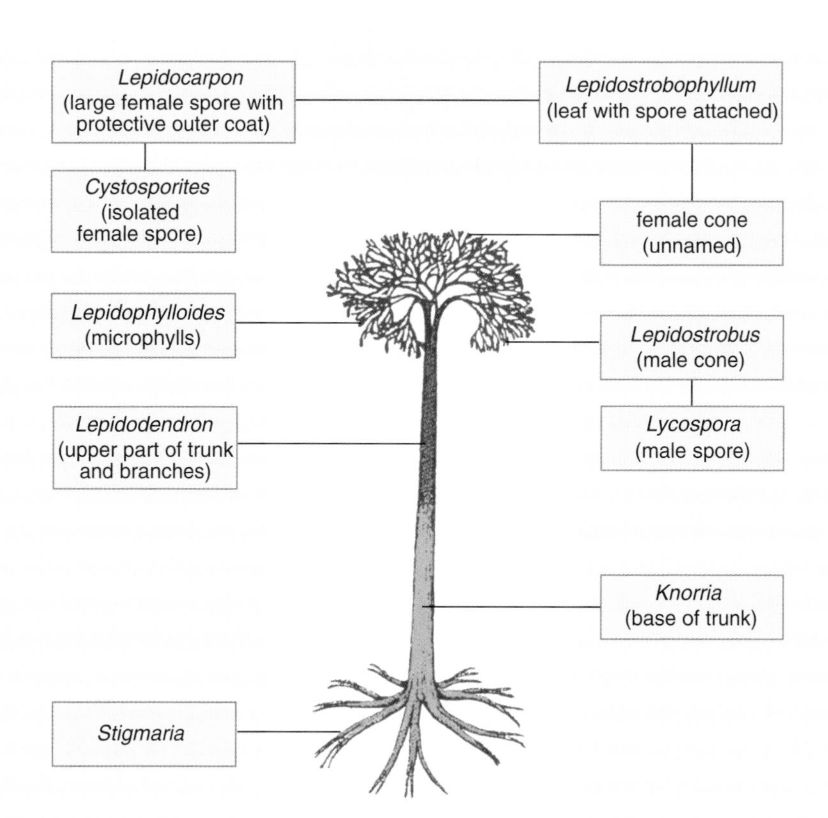

Figure 3.26 Reconstruction of a *Lepidodendron* tree, showing the names used for different parts of the plant. See text for further explanation.

Lepidodendron and the other tree-sized lycopsids contributed large amounts of carbon to the peat swamps. They did this because they grew very rapidly and when they reached maturity they reproduced just once, and then the whole tree died. The outer part of the trunk was made up of material that was very slow to decay and so large amounts of it accumulated in the peat.

The biology of the *Lepidodendron* tree has been reconstructed in great detail because different parts of the tree are often preserved in mineral deposits, called **coal balls**, within the coal. The coal balls preserve even cellular detail (by permineralization) so we can reconstruct the tissues of this plant and interpret how it grew. Figure 3.27 shows an example of this exquisite preservation. It is a section through a *Stigmaria* rootlet preserved in a coal ball. Note that a large part of the cross-section has no sign of any cells. This is not simply a case of poor preservation because all the roots of this type so far found have exactly the same 'missing' cells. In life it was an air space, lacking any cells. Such spaces are also found in modern plants that dwell in swamps and marshes.

- Considering the swampy, rather stagnant conditions in which *Lepidodendron* lived, what do you think was the purpose of the air spaces in its roots?

- The air spaces enabled oxygen in air to pass down to the root tissues. Like us, all plant parts need oxygen to respire, even though parts like leaves give out oxygen during the day as a by-product of photosynthesis. Roots need oxygen or they will die, so the air spaces in the roots compensated for the low levels of oxygen in stagnant water.

The level of oxygen in the atmosphere reached an all-time high in the late Carboniferous, due in part to the enormous amount of photosynthesizing plant material.

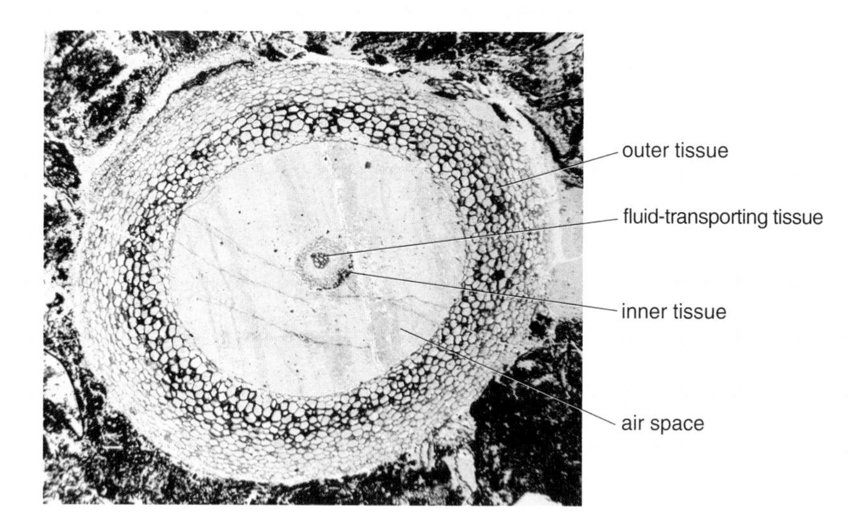

Figure 3.27 Cross-section through a rootlet of *Stigmaria* preserved in a coal ball. Diameter 5 mm.

- Today oxygen forms 20.9% of the atmosphere. What percentage did atmospheric oxygen possibly peak at in the late Carboniferous?

- Atmospheric oxygen may have peaked at about 30%, according to some investigators (*Atlas*, p.81). (If so, this raises interesting questions about how forest fires, started by lightning, for example, ever became extinguished as hot dry wood so readily bursts into flame in this concentration of oxygen.)

- What feature observed in well-preserved fossil plant leaves allows us to estimate relative levels of carbon dioxide and, by implication, oxygen in ancient times?

- The density of pores (stomata) in leaves, which varies in proportion to the level of carbon dioxide (*Atlas*, p.81).

- A fossil late Carboniferous dragonfly with a wingspan of 60 cm is pictured on p.85 of the *Atlas*. Given the fact that the oxygen which insects require for metabolism has to pass down tiny tubes in their exoskeleton to the tissues that use it, can you suggest a connection that might link exceptionally high levels of atmospheric oxygen to the evolution of giant dragonflies such as this?

- To stay in the air, flying insects burn up much oxygen in their muscles (as does a helicopter burning fuel in its engine). The maximum size of flying insects (and some other arthropods) is limited by the extent to which oxygen can reach the tissues (e.g. muscles) that use it. A higher oxygen level would have helped to increase the efficiency of the dragonfly's metabolism and allowed the evolution of larger size.

As you can see from the reconstructed coal forest on pp.84–85 of the *Atlas*, *Lepidodendron* was not the only type of plant that contributed to coal. *Sigillaria* was another tree-sized lycopsid, though unlike *Lepidodendron*, its 'leaf cushions' where microphylls were attached are arranged in vertical rows (*Atlas*, pp.84–85). There were also many ferns; a fossil of one type is shown on p.80 of the *Atlas*.

- What two other plant genera are named in the reconstructed forest on pp.84–85 of the *Atlas*, and to which major plant group does each belong?

- *Medullosa*, a pteridosperm (Section 3.7); *Calamites*, a sphenopsid (horsetail) (Section 3.7 and Figure 3.19b).

3.9 The Permian Period

Read the *Atlas*, pp.86–87.

Figure 3.28 Detail of part of a Permian fish from County Durham, England. The scales of such fish are much thicker than those of today's more familiar fish. Field of view 3 cm.

A major event that affected Permian life was the formation of the supercontinent of **Pangea** (*Atlas G*, pp.212, 214), which had begun to assemble in Carboniferous times. Pangea was to last for about 100 million years before beginning to break up in the early Jurassic.

- Which continents merged to form Pangea?

- The northern continents of Eurasia (Europe and Asia, without India) and Laurentia (North America, *Atlas G*, p.211) merged with the southern continent of Gondwana (*Atlas G*, p.209, *Atlas*, p.86).

The extent of Pangea can best be appreciated by looking at the whole-world map on the top right of p.29 of the *Atlas*. In the northern part of Pangea, the vast continental interior became hot and dry, especially in the tropics. The late Carboniferous to early Permian ice cap shrank, the humid coal forests and swamps diminished in extent, and many shallow seas evaporated, leaving extensive deposits of salt across Laurentia (the yellow areas on the globe, *Atlas*, p.86). These environmental changes favoured plants and animals that were better adapted to drier conditions, such as the seed-bearing gymnosperms (Section 3.7) and the egg-laying reptiles.

- Which extinct plant has Permian and Triassic fossils on so many different continents today that it has been used as evidence that all those continents were once joined together?

- The seed fern, *Glossopteris* (*Atlas*, p.87).

As we shall see in Section 3.10, at the end of the Permian an estimated 95% of marine species became extinct, and, as we calculated earlier in Question 3.4, there was a 65% decrease in the number of vertebrate families (both marine and land-based). One of the factors involved in this mass extinction was a huge reduction in the total area of shallow shelf seas that fringed the continents as the supercontinent was formed.

3.9.1 Ancient mammal relatives

Read the *Atlas*, pp.88–89.

The popular image of extinct reptiles tends to be dominated by the dinosaurs. However, especially during Permian and Triassic times, before dinosaurs came to dominate land environments, a group of egg-laying animals known as the **synapsids** (*Atlas G*, p.214) flourished. These synapsids are sometimes called '**mammal-like reptiles**' because they show certain mammal-like features, especially in their teeth. Although the *Atlas* (p.88) says the 'synapsids were never true reptiles', they are often treated as reptiles, as they are (for simplicity) in Figure 3.14.

Most reptiles, like crocodiles, have similar, peg-shaped, teeth in their mouths. Food is simply torn off and swallowed. Being cold blooded, they do not need continuous, high rates of energy output from their food; they can afford to consume large amounts quickly and leave the lengthy digestive process for their stomachs to deal with.

Consequently, a single large meal may last for several days. Different tooth shapes, as seen in the synapsids, especially the more advanced ones called **therapsids**, allow for varied functions. Small incisor-like teeth at the front of the mouth are used for holding, larger canines help in stabbing and killing prey, and molar-like cheek teeth help crush or chop and grind food before swallowing. The breakdown of food into small pieces with a large surface area allows faster processing of food in the stomach, leading to quicker release of its stored energy. For eating plants, some of the synapsids evolved curious, parrot-like beaks, e.g. *Lystrosaurus* (*Atlas*, p.88).

Although they did not include spectacularly large animals like the dinosaurs, the synapsids were a diverse group which ranged in size from small pig-sized creatures like *Robertia* (see panorama, *Atlas*, p.89) to the hippopotamus-sized *Kannemeyeria*, and *Moschops* which grew up to 5 m long. The sail-backed **pelycosaurs** (early synapsids) were highly successful, and *Edaphosaurus* (*Atlas*, p.86) and *Dimetrodon* (*Atlas*, p.89) both reached 3 m in length. Pelycosaurs are often mistakenly called dinosaurs, e.g. in cartoons and as plastic models in cereal packets.

- Which group of synapsids is of particular evolutionary interest as they gave rise to the first mammals in the late Triassic, as well as outlasting all other synapsids into late Jurassic times?

- The cynodonts (*Atlas*, p.89 and *Atlas G*, p.207), a group of therapsids. Incidentally, the *Atlas Glossary* entry for therapsids on p.215 should give their age range as late Permian to *late Jurassic*, which is when the cynodonts died out.

3.10 Extinctions are forever

In the early nineteenth century, scientists gradually became aware that the fossil record was far older and richer than previously thought, and that it could provide a huge amount of information about the history of the Earth and the course of life through time. On pp.102–103 of the *Atlas* (and Section 1.5) we saw that only gradually did early nineteenth century naturalists accept that species had become extinct. Although the awareness of the fact of extinction, and of the immense age of the Earth ('deep time'), were both major advances in scientific understanding, they were not sudden leaps following one particular observation or experiment. Each of these crucially important concepts took a long time to become established as the tide of evidence came slowly in. It eventually became clear that extinction, like death, is a normal aspect of the history of life. In fact, the vast majority of species that have ever existed — probably 99% — have become extinct.

Extinction is the complete, global end of the line for a species; it leaves no descendent individuals anywhere. It's very important to distinguish the *local* extinction of a species from true, *global* extinction. For example, the Large Blue butterfly used to be seen in English meadows in the early part of the twentieth century. Its life cycle was intimately associated with a species of ant that itself died out locally due to a change of grazing practice. The Large Blue became locally extinct in Britain in 1979, but it still lives in France, and elsewhere in Europe, and may yet do so again in England if conditions improve for it. Also, a species that has with time evolved directly *into* another species has also not become extinct in one crucial sense: it is not the end of the line. In this case the lineage has simply been sufficiently transformed for the descendants to be recognized as a different species, a phenomenon called **pseudoextinction**.

At any time in the history of life some species will be in the process of becoming extinct, and others will be originating. The fossil record shows that there has always been a normal, 'background' rate of both speciation (the formation of new species) and extinction of species. The majority of past species extinctions have been part of this 'background' rate of extinction. Early in the nineteenth century, however, it was recognized that, from time to time, many groups disappeared from the fossil record more or less together, never to be found again in younger rocks. It was partly for this reason that many of the boundaries between one geological period and another were constructed. Geologically rapid, major reductions in the diversity of life on a global scale are called **mass extinctions**.

Although in our journey through time we have only reached the end of the Palaeozoic Era, it is useful to put this mass extinction into perspective by considering others too. We will, of course, return to mass extinctions later, especially the one at the end of the Cretaceous (Section 4.11).

Two of the most severe mass extinctions were used in the nineteenth century to mark the end, not just of periods, but of eras — the Palaeozoic Era and the Mesozoic Era, i.e. the end of the Permian Period and the end of the Cretaceous Period. Although the mass extinction that ended the Cretaceous Period, 65 Ma ago, is the most famous of them all (because dinosaurs were its most notable victims), the mass extinction that ended the Permian Period was even more severe. The loss of marine animal species in the late Permian has been estimated to be as high as 95%, compared with 70% loss of marine animal species in the late Cretaceous. Such estimates of species extinctions are, however, subject to many uncertainties.

- Look at the chart on p.90 of the *Atlas* which relates to genera, not species. What percentage of marine invertebrate genera became extinct at the end of (a) the Permian and (b) the Cretaceous?

- (a) 68% (b) 43%.

- Why do you think the estimated number of genera that became extinct at these times is less than the estimated number of species that became extinct?

- A genus usually contains more than one species (Section 1.3). And just because a species becomes extinct does not mean that the whole genus (containing other species) becomes extinct too. The genus will survive as long as any one of its species persists.

In the same way, a genus is more likely to become extinct than a whole family because a family normally encompasses a number of genera, and all these genera would have to become extinct before the family itself does. Patterns of extinction thus differ for different taxonomic levels, depending on the severity of the crisis: minor extinction events are less likely to eliminate higher taxa above the level of species, such as families, than would mass extinctions. Estimates of the proportions of taxa that become extinct tend to be more accurate for higher taxa (e.g. families) than lower taxa (e.g. species).

In the end-Permian extinction, as many as 57% of marine families perished. As far as families are concerned, there have been five especially severe mass extinctions in the Phanerozoic — the '**Big Five**': in the late Ordovician, late Devonian, late Permian, late Triassic, and late Cretaceous (see Box 3.2 *Some casualties of the Big Five Phanerozoic extinctions*).

- Look at the chart on p.90 of the *Atlas*. How does the above list of the 'Big Five' compare with the data based on genera?

- The late Devonian mass extinction — the second of the Big Five — does not appear quite as severe as two extinction events in the Cambrian when over 40% of marine invertebrate genera were lost. (This apparent discrepancy arises because, by the late Devonian, life had become much more diverse than in the Cambrian, with far more species in total, and, on average, more species per genus. The late Devonian mass extinction eliminated a far higher number of taxa in absolute terms.)

Box 3.2 Some casualties of the Big Five Phanerozoic extinctions

Late Ordovician Many types of trilobites, brachiopods, graptolites, echinoderms and corals.

Late Devonian Many marine families, especially those of tropical reef-dwelling organisms such as corals, brachiopods, bivalves and sponges.

Late Permian 57% of marine families, especially those from low latitudes. Virtually all corals became extinct, and reefs were eliminated. Trilobites and water-scorpions (eurypterids; *Atlas G*, p.208) disappeared totally. Crinoids, brachiopods, bivalves and gastropods suffered huge losses. Many groups of amphibians and reptiles perished; 70% of vertebrate genera living on land vanished.

Late Triassic Major losses among cephalopods, gastropods, brachiopods, bivalves, sponges and marine reptiles. On land many insect families became extinct, as did most mammal-like reptiles and large amphibians (though the extinction of these vertebrate groups does not show up well in Figure 3.14 as other reptile and amphibian families were originating at about the same time).

Late Cretaceous Whole groups that became extinct near (and not necessarily *at*) the end of the Cretaceous included ammonites, large marine reptiles such as plesiosaurs and mosasaurs, and, on land, dinosaurs and pterosaurs. Groups suffering major losses included microscopic marine plankton, brachiopods, bivalves and sea urchins. Vertebrate groups affected relatively *little* included fishes, amphibians, crocodiles, snakes, turtles and mammals. Flowering plants, including hardwood trees, suffered also, but mostly in the Northern Hemisphere.

None of the Big Five mass extinctions seems to have been instantaneous; in most cases it probably took from about 0.5 Ma to 1 Ma for all the losses to occur. And mass extinctions are probably not discrete phenomena, completely different from other extinctions, any more than there are clear boundaries between large and medium earthquakes, or between hurricanes and severe storms. There seems to be a continuous spectrum of extinction severity from background rates at one end, through times of moderate extinction, to mass extinctions at the other. Some of the groups lost in mass extinctions were already far from flourishing. For example, the decline of trilobites was well underway before their eventual demise in the late Permian.

Can one make any generalizations about the victims of mass extinctions? Well, it seems that large-bodied species tend to be more vulnerable than smaller bodied species, perhaps because they tend to be more specialized, have smaller population sizes, and slower rates of population increase. Tropical organisms, at least those in the sea, appear to be more vulnerable than those of higher latitudes.

- Imagine a species of marine snail that can live today only in the hot, shallow seas found immediately around the Equator. Would an increase or decrease in global temperature be more likely to threaten this tropical species with extinction, and why?

- If global temperature were reduced, the snails would have nowhere to go that was warm enough; they are already in the hottest environment. If, however, there were an *increase* in temperature, the snails might well, over generations, be able to migrate away from equatorial latitudes to where the water was cooler, or perhaps migrate into deeper, cooler water on the Equator. Other things being equal, tropical species may therefore be more susceptible to global cooling than to global warming. (As always, however, things are not so simple; coral reefs are dying off at an alarming rate due to abnormally *high* recent sea surface temperatures, and several coral species have become regionally extinct.)

The average duration of a marine invertebrate species in the fossil record (from origin to extinction) is about 5 Ma, though there is much variation about this mean. Interestingly, many of these fossil species, having made their first appearance, show very little change (in their hard parts at least) before becoming extinct several million years later. Continuous, gradual transitions from one species to another are only rarely found in the fossil record. This may, however, be partly due to the lack of fossils from on land in the tropics (see Question 1.2c) and from the deeper sea — relatively stable environments where evolution may tend to be more gradual and continuous than in shallow marine environments.

3.10.1 Searching for the causes of mass extinctions

Reasons invoked in the past for the extinction of the dinosaurs included constipation and stupidity.

- Apart from being untestable, why would such suggestions be inadequate as explanations for *mass* extinctions?

- Any proposed mechanism(s) for mass extinctions must embrace many groups, and operate over a wide area, both on land and in the sea.

- In what ways, other than extinction, might a species respond to severe environmental change affecting its habitat?

- A species may be able to migrate into more favourable areas, or, in the longer term, evolve adaptations to the new environment.

What kind of environmental changes, then, are so severe that large numbers of species cannot migrate away from those changes, or adapt to them? The most plausible hypotheses are those such as rapid changes in global temperature or oxygen levels — as opposed to, say, disease or predation, which are unlikely to affect many thousands of species at the same time.

In addition to the possible influence of extraterrestrial events, the Earth-bound causes most often proposed for mass extinctions include:

- climate change, either greenhouse warming or cooling and drying (drought);
- sea-level rise or fall;
- changes in oceanic circulation, leading to lower levels of dissolved oxygen in shallow waters;
- changes in atmospheric chemistry;
- intense volcanic activity.

Most of these causes are not mutually exclusive; for example, cooling and widespread glaciation leads to lower sea level because water is transferred from the oceans and locked up as ice on land; volcanic activity could promote climate change and also pollute the atmosphere, causing acid rain, for example.

The mass extinction at the end of the Permian may have occurred when several changes in the physical environment coincided accidentally. There is currently no consensus about the mechanism(s) involved. There seems to have been a lowering of atmospheric oxygen levels linked to lowering of sea level and changes in oceanic circulation patterns as Pangea assembled (Section 3.9), combined with adverse effects from extensive volcanic eruptions (flood basalts) in Siberia. The total area of shallow shelf seas became greatly reduced as the continents merged into Pangea. The precise pattern and likely causes of this most severe of all extinctions are being intensively researched. Strata that span the Permian–Triassic boundary are rare and often poorly accessible, but the most recent studies indicate that the extinction event was much more abrupt than previously thought. Instead of the extinctions occurring over perhaps as much as 10 million years (as it says on p.197 of the *Atlas*), many species may have disappeared over an interval of no more than 100 000 years, and possibly much less.

- Look at Figure 3.15. To what extent were the major groups of land plants affected by the end Permian mass extinction?

- Very little, at least not at the taxonomic level of major groups represented in the diagram. (There were some extinctions in some major groups, but overall plants were far less badly affected than animals.)

The late Ordovician mass extinction of marine organisms was almost certainly linked to widespread glaciation and a large fall in sea level. Climate change is also implicated in both the late Devonian and late Triassic mass extinctions. As is mentioned on pp.90–91 of the *Atlas*, and as we'll see again later (Section 4.11), there is overwhelming evidence that a large meteorite hit the Earth at the end of the Cretaceous Period, and that it caused some, but by no means all, of the late Cretaceous extinctions. This is currently the only mass extinction for which the influence of a meteorite is strongly implicated.

Given a long enough time interval, an 'exceedingly unlikely event' on a short time-scale, such as the impact of a huge meteorite or an enormous volcanic eruption, is very likely to happen at some time within that interval. If the impact at the end of the Cretaceous did indeed cause many extinctions (Section 4.11), then such catastrophes must play an important role in evolution. Conditions after the impact may have been both drastically and *randomly* changed from conditions prevailing for millions of years before. The extinction of some species may therefore have been more a matter of bad luck than bad genes. As we'll see in Section 5.2, new evolutionary opportunities then arose for some of the lucky survivors.

The positive and negative feedback mechanisms in the Earth's ocean–atmosphere system, and in its ecosystems, are immensely complex. Establishing the full chain of cause and effect during extinctions, and precisely which biological attributes — or lack of them — led to the demise of a particular species, is a difficult if not impossible task, even for most extinctions taking place around the turn of the twenty-first century.

3.10.2 Extinction today

Estimating the rate at which species are becoming extinct today is very difficult, not least because we do not know how many species there are to start with: estimates range from about 5 million to 30 million species.

- Mammals and birds probably provide the best data of any groups. Why do you think this is?

- They are particularly well-studied, being relatively large, conspicuous and mostly living on land, and in the past many have attracted attention as a human food source.

The average duration of mammal and bird species in the fossil record is much nearer 0.5–1 Ma than the 5 Ma for marine invertebrate species, partly perhaps because their complex social behaviour favours rapid evolution and speciation. Many large mammals and large flightless birds became extinct between 15 000 and 10 000 years ago, and there is evidence that human hunting activities, as well as climate changes, were responsible. Today, there are about 13 400 living species of birds and mammals, and at least 100 species have become extinct during the last 100 years alone through human activities. The rate of extinction is escalating, and in a few decades the average time remaining before a typical bird or mammal species becomes extinct is projected to be 200–400 years; this is approaching a factor of 10 000 times faster than the background rates seen in the fossil record. The loss among mammals and birds may also be broadly representative of other groups of animals, and plants. Conservative estimates of current total extinction rates are 5–50 species *per day*. Many biologists believe that this general time in Earth history could appear as another mass extinction in the geological record — 'the **Sixth Extinction**' to add to the previous Big Five. As a warning, the fossil record shows that recovery from earlier mass extinctions is extremely slow by human time-scales. The regeneration of biodiversity, and re-establishment of communities such as reefs, typically takes 5–10 Ma.

Now watch the Video Programme *Lost Worlds*. This was originally produced for the course S103 *Discovering Science*. The programme looks mainly at aspects of extinction as seen in the fossil record. As you watch it, make a note of points that will enable you to answer the following questions.

Question 3.5 The acceptance of extinction is described in the programme *Lost Worlds* as a 'huge conceptual shift'. According to the programme, why did many people at the start of the nineteenth century find it impossible to accept the accumulating evidence that some fossils were the remains of *extinct* species? ◀

Question 3.6 To whom do the following descriptions apply? Note that some extra information is given here beyond that given in the programme.

(a) A brilliant Frenchman who lived from 1769–1832, he is widely regarded as founding the two sciences of comparative anatomy and palaeontology. About 1800, he argued that the many different fossil bones and teeth which were similar to, but different from, the bones and teeth of large modern animals (such as elephants) must belong to *extinct* species; the animals from which these fossils came would simply be too conspicuous to have been overlooked by travellers throughout the world. From his work in the Paris area, he concluded that there had been a series of catastrophes which had swept away whole living populations, and that such catastrophes were a common feature in Earth's history.

(b) A Scottish geologist, originally a lawyer, who lived from 1797–1875. His treatise *Principles of Geology* (1830–1833) was highly influential, being read, for example, by Darwin during his voyage on *The Beagle*. He vigorously opposed the ideas of catastrophism, promoting the idea that 'The present is the key to the past', and argued that the Earth was very much older than the 6000 years many then believed it to be. ◀

Question 3.7 Apart from numerous problems caused by the incompleteness of the fossil record and the geological record in general, why is it so difficult to establish the causes of extinctions? ◀

Question 3.8 According to the programme, why did mammoths (cold-adapted elephants) become extinct? ◀

Now read the *Atlas*, pp.196–197, which underpin some of the important points in this section.

3.11 Summary of Palaeozoic life

During the Cambrian explosion, starting about 545 Ma ago, animals with hard parts, and animals capable of making complex trace fossils, proliferated in a sudden burst of evolution. From their fossil record, almost all animal phyla seem to appear at this time, but many had probably diverged from each other much earlier; previously lacking shells or teeth, and possibly being much smaller, their preservation potential before then was minimal. The exceptionally well preserved mid Cambrian Burgess Shale fossils reveal a very wide diversity of Cambrian animals, including *Pikaia*, a chordate close to our earliest vertebrate ancestor.

From the early Cambrian into the Ordovician there was a massive increase in the abundance and diversity of readily fossilizable shallow marine organisms. Some such groups were confined to the Palaeozoic, including, for example, trilobites, graptolites and jawless armoured fishes.

A mass extinction of marine life occurred at the end of the Ordovician, for which an Ice Age was almost certainly responsible. Groups like the trilobites and graptolites suffered greatly and never fully recovered their diversity, but others such as the molluscs (including bivalves, gastropods and cephalopods), corals, and fishes subsequently continued to expand. The shallow Silurian seas teemed with life, now preserved in deposits such as the Wenlock Limestone. Another mass extinction, also one of the 'Big Five' of the Phanerozoic, occurred in the late Devonian; it especially affected tropical reef-dwelling organisms.

The main invasion of the land in Silurian times, initially by small plants such as *Cooksonia*, and by detritus-eating arthropods, opened up a vast new range of ecological niches. Jawless fish swarmed into freshwater rivers and lakes, to be followed by jawed fish, which were much more efficient predators. In plants, competition for light soon forced structural improvements for increased height, stem strength and better reproduction. The forests of the late Palaeozoic (Devonian, Carboniferous and Permian) became populated with distinctive plant groups that provided the basis for the terrestrial food chain, e.g. clubmosses and horsetails, few of which survive today, and seed ferns, which are extinct.

After emerging in late Devonian times, tetrapod communities were initially dominated by large amphibians, especially in Carboniferous and Permian times. The first reptiles appeared in the early Carboniferous; their key innovation was a shelled amniotic egg, freeing them from dependence on nearby bodies of water for reproduction. By the Permian, the synapsids, such as the large, sail-backed pelycosaurs and the more advanced therapsids, had appeared; they evolved increasingly mammal-like features such as differentiated teeth.

During early Carboniferous times, the existence of widespread, shallow tropical seas again promoted the development of coral reefs, which in turn supported a huge diversity of reef-dwelling organisms such as bryozoans, trilobites, molluscs, echinoderms (especially crinoids), brachiopods, and a great variety of fish. In the late Carboniferous equatorial forests and low-lying swamps, massive amounts of plant debris accumulated, later becoming coal.

By the end of the Palaeozoic, many of the major and subsequently important groups of animals and plants had evolved. Important exceptions include the modern amphibians (frogs, toads and newts), dinosaurs, crocodiles, lizards, snakes, turtles, tortoises, mammals, birds and flowering plants, all of which were to appear in the Mesozoic.

The end of Permian times saw the final assembly of the supercontinent Pangea, a lowering of sea level, a huge reduction in the area of shallow shelf seas, and the eruption of enormous thicknesses of basalt lavas in Siberia, all of which must have led to climate change. Although the chain of cause and effect is not certain, the end of the Palaeozoic Era was marked by the biggest extinction event in the history of life, with 57% of marine families and 70% of land vertebrate genera becoming extinct. Among the marine groups that disappeared forever were the rugose and tabulate corals, trilobites and water scorpions, and many groups of brachiopods, crinoids, bivalves and gastropods were drastically reduced. Plants, by contrast, were relatively little affected.

4 Life in the Mesozoic

4.1 The Triassic Period

Read the *Atlas*, pp.92–93.

In the Triassic Period, life rather slowly recovered from the devastating extinction event that marked the end of the Palaeozoic Era. Many groups never regained their former diversity, even if they survived. There were, however, many significant innovations during Triassic times.

- Which major 'new wave' grouping of reptiles emerged during the Triassic that included the dinosaurs, the flying pterosaurs (*Atlas G*, p.213) and crocodiles (including the crocodile-like phytosaurs, *Atlas*, p.93)?

- The archosaurs (*Atlas G*, p.204).

During the Triassic, the cynodonts (Section 3.9.1) diversified and replaced the older synapsids of the Permian. The skull alone of the large carnivore *Cynognathus* (illustrated in the *Atlas*, p.92) was 40 cm long. You may have been surprised to read that among the characteristics possessed by *Cynognathus* was possibly a covering of hair, which today is a diagnostic character of mammals. We will return to this topic shortly, in Section 4.4.

Nothosaurs were marine predators that arose and died out within the Triassic Period. The nothosaur illustrated on p.92 of the *Atlas* was about 1.2 m long, though some were over 4 m. In addition to other new marine reptile groups such as the phytosaurs and turtles, the seas became filled with new groups of bony fish and cephalopods, especially new groups of the coiled ammonoids (the group which later included the first true ammonites in the Jurassic) as well as the precursors of the belemnites (*Atlas G*, p.205, Box 3.1 and Section 4.6). There were apparently no corals in the early Triassic; modern corals (scleractinians; Box 3.1) are known only from the mid Triassic onwards. Bivalve and gastropod molluscs diversified, like many other groups taking advantage of niches vacated by previously successful and dominant groups that had disappeared or gone into decline at the end of the Permian. On land, primitive conifers (*Atlas G*, p.206; Section 3.7) were able to colonize dry upland landscapes and new cycads (*Atlas G*, p.207; Section 3.7) flourished, whilst swampy areas saw the first of the modern amphibians — frogs.

4.2 Dinosaurs

From the largest animals ever to have lived on land to beasts no bigger than a chicken, dinosaurs were certainly an extraordinarily diverse and successful group. They thrived for over 150 million years, from the late Triassic to the end of the Cretaceous. They included carnivores (meat eaters), herbivores (plant eaters) and a few omnivores (mixed diet). Although they never took to the air or to the oceans, dinosaurs filled many of the niches possible for large land vertebrates. And in an important sense the dinosaurs are still with us: one group became covered in feathers and today we call their highly successful descendants birds (Section 4.5.1).

Note: there is no need to get bogged down in this (and later sections) trying to remember all the dinosaur names or worrying how to pronounce them. You may find it useful to add your own annotations to Figure 4.2, e.g. indicating with an abbreviation which groups are meat eaters, and which plant eaters.

An important early discovery about dinosaurs concerned the structure of their pelvic girdles, i.e. the part of the skeleton where the hind limbs are attached (Box 4.1). Since 1887 dinosaurs have been divided into two main groups — **saurischians** (*Atlas G*, p.213) and **ornithischians** (*Atlas G*, p.212). The '-ischian' part of these names is pronounced 'iskian'.

- Without going into the names of individual bones, what is the key difference between saurischians and ornithischians?

Box 4.1 What makes a dinosaur?

The British comparative anatomist and palaeontologist Richard Owen (*Atlas*, p.200) coined the name Dinosauria (from the Greek, meaning 'terrible lizards') in 1842 for a group of fossils which he considered to be distinct from all other known reptiles. Critically, Owen showed that these large-bodied, extinct reptiles were able to walk with their legs tucked in directly below the body. By contrast, living reptiles have limbs that stick out to the side of the body so they walk in a sprawling, sinuous motion.

In 1887, the British palaeontologist Harry Govier Seeley showed that there were two consistent types of pelvic structure to be found in dinosaurs. One type was much like that of living reptiles, with the pubis bone directed mostly forwards and another bone, the ischium, directed mostly backwards (Figure 4.1a); he named this the saurischian ('reptile-hipped') type. The other kind, superficially resembling the bird pelvis, had the shaft of the pubis lying backwards next to the ischium; Seeley called this the ornithischian ('bird-hipped') type (Figure 4.1b). Thus he distinguished two fundamentally separate groups of dinosaurs, the Saurischia and Ornithischia. There are certain other differences between the two groups, but they share many skeletal features in common. The ornithischians were all herbivores and walked either on two feet (bipedal) or on four feet (quadrupedal). The saurischians included both carnivores, which were all bipedal, and herbivores, which were all quadrupedal.

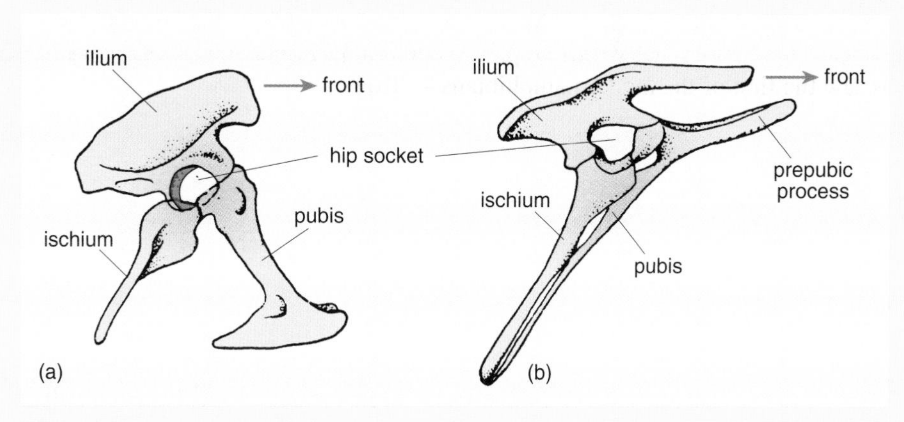

Figure 4.1 The pelvic structure of the two main types of dinosaurs: (a) a saurischian dinosaur; (b) an ornithischian dinosaur.

- The saurischians had a pelvis which did not differ much from that of normal, living reptiles, whereas the ornithischians had a pelvis superficially more like that of birds (Box 4.1).

Now read the *Atlas*, p.113.

As we'll see in Section 4.8, dinosaur remains were first recognized in Mesozoic strata of southern England in the early decades of the nineteenth century. The pioneering studies of dinosaurs, which took place in Britain, culminated in the construction of the world's first theme park around the relocated Crystal Palace in south London. Opened in 1854, the park included the first life-size reconstructions of dinosaurs ever attempted, and they are still there. With hindsight, these reconstructions have some understandable errors (Section 4.8). A few years later, in 1858, a more complete skeleton of a dinosaur was found in New Jersey, USA. Named *Hadrosaurus*, it clearly had hind limbs that were much bigger than its forelimbs, and so it was reconstructed with a two-legged, kangaroo-like posture. Within the next decade or so, the discovery of far more complete dinosaurs in the Midwest of the USA meant that the focus of dinosaur research shifted to America (*Atlas*, pp.113, 183). Since the early nineteenth century, our view of dinosaurs and their evolution has radically changed. Today, although we are still far from knowing the full story, our understanding of the main groups is becoming much clearer.

The ancestral (saurischian) pelvic structure is found in all the archosaur reptiles of the early Triassic, when the archosaurs split into several groups, leading to crocodiles, pterosaurs and dinosaurs (Figure 4.2). The saurischian condition is thus found in the first dinosaurs of late Triassic times (such as the ceratosaur *Coelophysis*, see below). There are two main groups of saurischians — **theropods** and **sauropods** (Figure 4.2). The theropods (*Atlas G*, p.215) were bipedal and mostly carnivores, among the best known of which are the tyrannosaurs (*Atlas G*, p.215). The sauropods were quadrupedal plant eaters (*Atlas G*, p.213) that ranged from late Triassic to Cretaceous times. (Actually, the late Triassic and early Jurassic forms of these are known as prosauropods and although there is not yet a complete sequence of forms linking these to the more advanced sauropods, for simplicity they are shown in Figure 4.2 as a single group.)

The sauropods include the largest ever land-living animals. Some had enormous bulk, with body weights exceeding 80 tonnes. The stresses on the limbs and girdles were immense, as can be sensed from the giant sauropod *Supersaurus* leg bones shown on p.113 of the *Atlas*. Inevitably, the structure of the toes, limb joints, shoulder and pelvic girdles became adapted to hold up such a massive body and allow it to be moved. The sideways-sprawling limbs of modern reptiles such as lizards and crocodiles are not adapted to cope with such stresses (for comparison, see the picture of an iguana limb on p.112 of the *Atlas*).

The ornithischians evolved at the same time as the saurischians (late Triassic) but few became fossilized until early Jurassic times, when the heterodontosaurids appeared (Figure 4.2). The ornithischians were all plant eaters and are best known for the array of dinosaurs they produced in late Jurassic and Cretaceous times, ranging from bipedal hadrosaurs (*Atlas G*, p.209) to quadrupedal stegosaurs (*Atlas*, p.99 and *Atlas G*, p.214). We will look in more detail at Cretaceous dinosaurs in Sections 4.8.1 and 4.8.2.

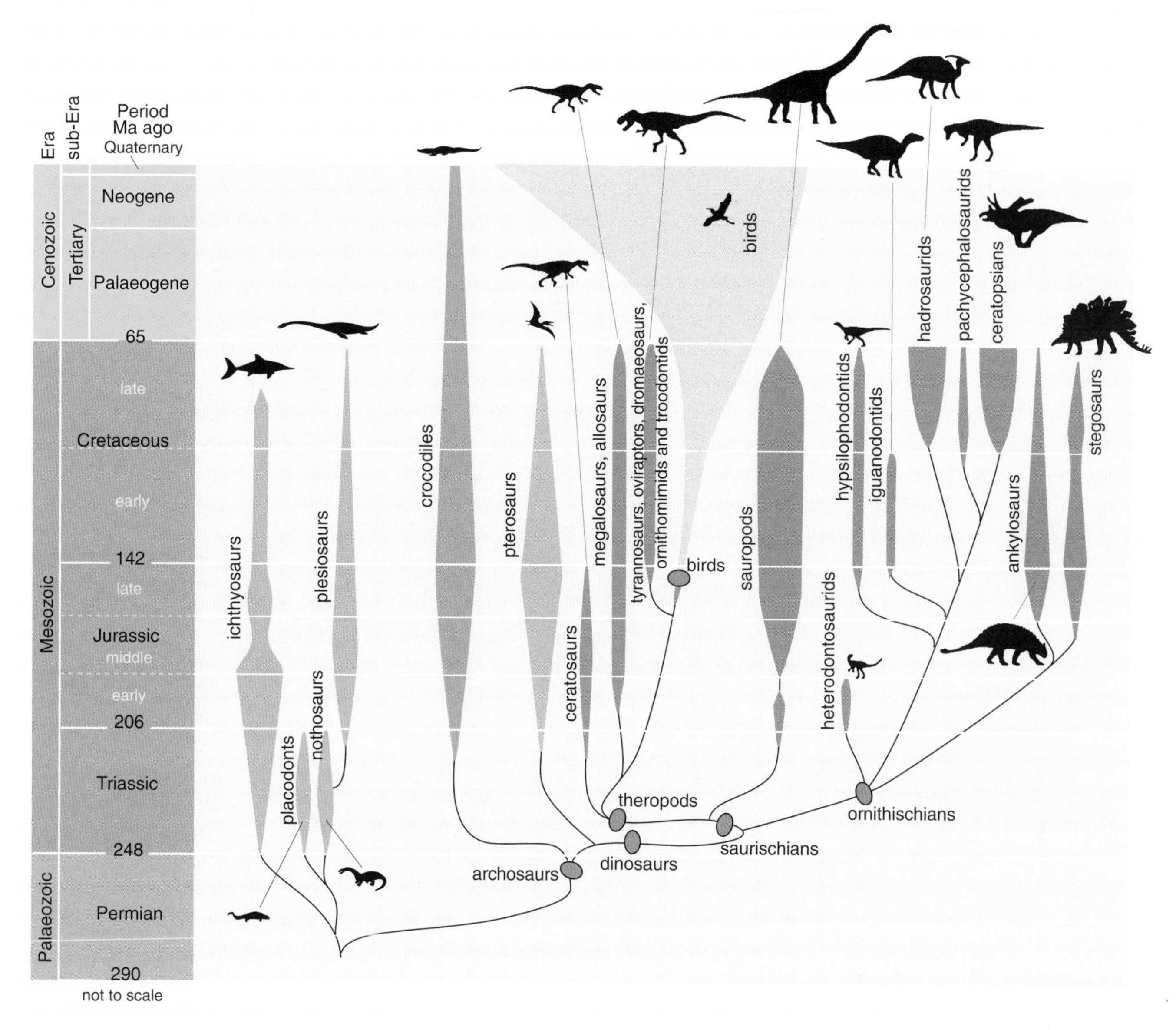

Figure 4.2 The time ranges (solid spindles) and probable evolutionary connections (thin lines) of the main groups of dinosaurs, some other reptile groups, and birds. The width of each spindle gives a rough indication of diversity. The silhouettes show approximate relative sizes of typical representatives. The names by the brown ovals show the group name for all the descendants from that ancestor. The time at which such ancestors existed is uncertain and shown only very approximately.

- Look at Figure 4.2. After the end of the Triassic, when were there (a) the least number, and (b) the largest number, of dinosaur groups?

- (a) There were only four dinosaur groups in the early and middle Jurassic; (b) there were nine dinosaur groups in the late Cretaceous (megalosaurs/allosaurs, tyrannosaurs, etc., sauropods, hysilophodontids, hadrosaurids, pachycephalosaurids, ceratopsians, ankylosaurs and stegosaurs).

Now read the *Atlas*, pp.94–95.

One of the best known early saurischian dinosaurs is *Coelophysis*, a small theropod **ceratosaur** (see Figure 4.2) from the late Triassic of North America. Insights about its way of life come from over a thousand specimens recovered from Ghost Ranch in New Mexico, USA.

- *Coelophysis* is described as a fast-moving, hunting meat eater. What evidence is given for this behaviour?

- *Coelophysis* had a slender muscular body, with hollow, light bones and long legs, and its narrow skull was armed with many sharp, dagger-shaped teeth. Other evidence of meat-eating is that some *Coelophysis* individuals had eaten smaller members of their own species (*Atlas*, pp.94–95).

- Most living reptile predators are solitary hunters. In what way was *Coelophysis* different?

- *Coelophysis* was probably a pack hunter, more typical of some smaller predatory mammals today (such as wolves) than any living reptiles.

Over the last couple of decades, ideas about the dinosaurs, their evolution, ways of life and extinction have been revolutionized. One of the most contentious issues has been whether or not the dinosaurs were warm blooded. It has been suggested that because many dinosaurs seem to have had lifestyles more analogous to mammals than living reptiles, they must have been warm blooded. The question particularly concerns the bipedal dinosaurs. Analysis of their trackways, especially those of small and medium-sized animals, suggests that some of them were capable of running at speeds approaching 40 km per hour, again more typical today of mammals or birds than reptiles.

Recent research has shown that for any large dinosaur living in warm climates, the mass of their bodies was so great that their body temperature would have stayed fairly constant without any internal heat production of the kind seen in mammals and birds. However, smaller dinosaurs, such as the hypsilophodonts (Sections 4.8.1 and 4.8.2), also show various signs of being highly active and perhaps warm-blooded animals. The current consensus is that, in terms of their physiology, dinosaurs were neither typically reptilian nor mammalian but probably occupied some intermediate position.

4.3 Flying and marine reptiles

Read the *Atlas*, pp.96–97 and pp.100–101.

Popular books on dinosaurs often include Mesozoic flying and marine reptiles such as pterosaurs and ichthyosaurs, respectively, although these groups were not dinosaurs. Their evolution was all part of the Triassic diversification of reptiles as a whole which led to reptilian dominance of so many ecological niches throughout the Mesozoic Era.

- What selective advantage did the evolution of special 'wing-like' structures suitable for gliding give to some reptiles, such as *Kuehneosaurus*?

- As they probably lived in trees, gliding allowed them to escape from predators (*Atlas*, p.96).

A number of unrelated reptile groups have taken up gliding since late Permian times. Active flight evolved in pterosaurs (*Atlas G*, p.213), and later independently in birds and bats (mammals). Active flying is very different from passive gliding and, as we shall see in Section 4.5.1, there is much debate about how winged flight originated in birds.

- What is the name given to the evolution of similar morphological features, such as wings or a streamlined body, in *unrelated* groups in response to the same environmental pressures?

- Convergent evolution (*Atlas*, p.97 and *Atlas G*, p.206).

A variety of Mesozoic reptile groups returned to the sea from where their tetrapod ancestors originated in the late Palaeozoic.

Question 4.1 Write down the five marine reptile groups mentioned in the *Atlas* on pp.96–97 and pp.100–101, and state their diet. How, in general, do we know the diet of such reptiles? ◀

In addition to these major marine reptile groups, the awesome mosasaurs (*Atlas G*, p.211) evolved later, in the Cretaceous.

- How did the ichthyosaurs (*Atlas G*, p.210; Figure 4.3) resolve the reproductive problem of being fully aquatic, ocean-going animals whilst also being amniote reptiles?

- The females gave birth to live young underwater (as is true of some sea snakes today); they did not need to lay shelled eggs on land (*Atlas*, pp.97, 100).

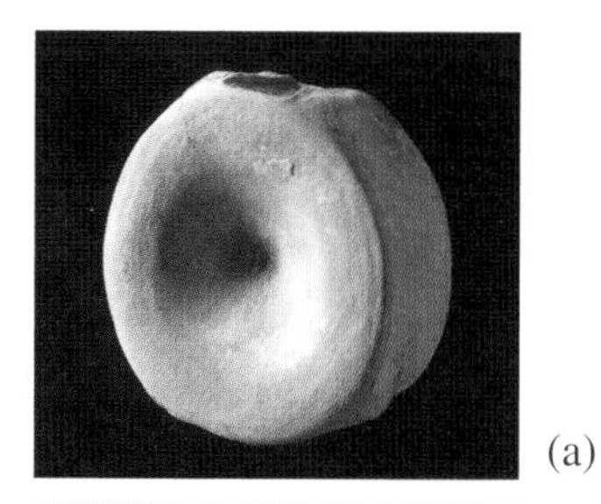
(a)

(b)

(c)

Figure 4.3 Three fossils representing ichthyosaurs that can quite commonly be found in Jurassic strata, especially washed out from clay-rich rocks on the Dorset and Yorkshire coasts. (a) A vertebra (6.5 cm); ichthyosaur vertebrae are typically dished in the centre (on both sides, i.e. front and back), unlike those of plesiosaurs, which are flatter; (b) a fragment of a bone from a rib cage (6 cm); (c) one of many bones from a paddle (4.5 cm). To see how these fossils relate to a complete ichthyosaur skeleton, look at the picture on p.97 of the *Atlas*.

4.4 Early mammals

Read the *Atlas*, pp.106–107.

Evolution of the full suite of mammalian characters took a very long time. Early traits such as tooth differentiation are found as far back as late Carboniferous times. By the mid Triassic, significant advances can be recognized in fossils of the cynodont synapsids. Apart from changes to their teeth, cynodonts evolved a number of important adaptations, giving them a selective edge among other tetrapods.

- What new cynodont feature allowed the separation of breathing from eating, so both could take place at the same time?

- A bony roof plate in the mouth, i.e. a secondary palate (which reptiles do not have) (*Atlas*, p.106).

The evidence that cynodonts such as *Cynognathus* (*Atlas*, p.92) were furry comes from the presence of small canals in the snout of the skull that, by analogy with today's mammals, indicate nerves that served whiskers. Some cynodonts almost certainly were warm blooded as well as having fur. So, given the well-documented, relatively gradual, progressive transition from reptiles to mammals, what criterion is used to distinguish the first mammals of the late Triassic from their mammal-like ancestors? It is simply the number of bones in the middle ear. Reptiles have a single ear bone, the stapes. Mammals, in contrast, have three ear bones, the malleus, incus

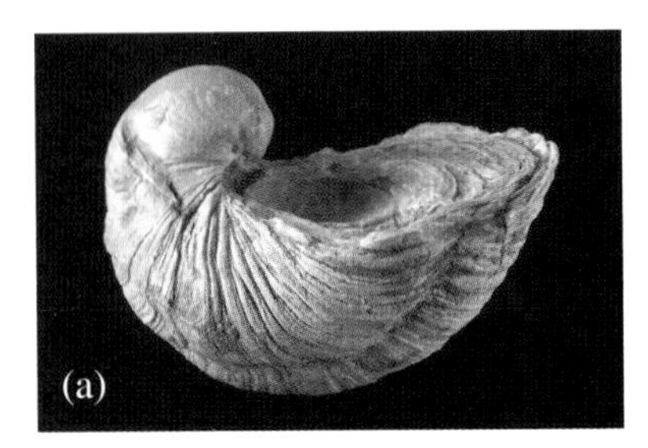

Figure 4.4 Three Jurassic fossils so common that they became part of ancient local folklore. (a) The bivalve mollusc, *Gryphaea arcuata* (5 cm); (b) a typical belemnite (cephalopod mollusc): this one is *Pachyteuthis abbreviata* (10 cm, incomplete); (c) the ammonite (cephalopod mollusc), *Dactylioceras commune* (8 cm).

and stapes. Surprising as it may seem, the two small bones that form the joint between the lower and upper jaws of reptiles became incorporated into the middle ear of mammals (as the malleus and incus).

Why was the preservation potential of early Mesozoic mammals so low, and what fossil evidence is usually all that remains?

The early mammals were mostly small (shrew-sized), with delicate bones. They were probably eaten whole by predators and scavengers. Consequently, the toughest, most indigestible parts of the skeleton such as teeth and jawbones were preferentially preserved (*Atlas*, p.107).

Despite the problematic nature of the early mammal record, it is clear that a wide range of mammal groups had evolved by the end of the Mesozoic. As the *Atlas* shows (pp.106–107), by the late Cretaceous there were multituberculates (now extinct; *Atlas G*, p.211), the surviving monotremes (*Atlas G*, p.211) and placental mammals (*Atlas G*, p.213), although the explosive early Tertiary diversification of placental mammals had yet to occur (Section 5.2). Marsupials (*Atlas G*, p.211), another group surviving today, had also appeared.

4.5 The Jurassic Period

Read the *Atlas*, pp.98–99.

Initially, life in the Jurassic Period was recovering from an extinction event that marked the end of Triassic times, when about 48% of the marine invertebrate genera were wiped out (*Atlas*, p.90; Box 3.2, Section 3.10). The diversity of vertebrate life on the land was also reduced (Figure 3.14), but recovery was rapid. Overall, Jurassic times saw a greater variety of life than at any previous time in Earth's history. Dinosaurs (Section 4.2) were just one of many flourishing vertebrate groups. Apart from the huge range of Mesozoic plants (Section 3.7), all the main vertebrate classes, including birds, had evolved by the late Jurassic, as had many modern insect groups and most groups of marine invertebrates.

Figure 4.4 (a–c) shows three commonly found Jurassic invertebrate fossils. What are their folklore nicknames?

(a) Devil's toenail; (b) thunderbolt; (c) snakestone (*Atlas*, p.99).

4.5.1 Solenhofen and *Archaeopteryx*

Read the *Atlas*, pp.104–105.

The Jurassic limestones of the region around Solenhofen in Bavaria, southern Germany, are unusual in that the quarried blocks are still split by hand, enabling many fossils to be retrieved that would otherwise remain undetected. Slabs of this fine-grained Solenhofen Limestone have been used in buildings for millennia, as witnessed by their presence in Roman baths, aqueducts and castles. It was also used by the Romans for drawing and carving, and in the nineteenth century for lithographic printing. In 1860, quarrying uncovered an astonishing fossil: a well-preserved feather (*Atlas* p.193). Six months later a skeleton of *Archaeopteryx*, perhaps the most famous fossil in the world, was found.

- What evolutionary connection was made by the discovery of *Archaeopteryx*, and why?
- The connection between reptiles and birds. *Archaeopteryx*, having feathers, was classified as the earliest known bird but it retained some distinctive reptilian characteristics.

The 'missing link' between reptiles and birds was suddenly no longer missing. As we saw in Section 1.7, this was timely because the finding of an intermediate form linking two major groups of organisms supported the then recently published theory of evolution by natural selection.

- What are the main reptilian, dinosaur-like, features of *Archaeopteryx*?
- A long bony tail, teeth, and curved claws on the forelimbs (*Atlas*, p.104).

- With which group of dinosaurs shown in Figure 4.2 do birds share their most recent common ancestor?
- The theropod group that includes the tyrannosaurs, oviraptors, dromaeosaurs, ornithomimids and troodontids.

Some of the smaller bipedal dinosaurs in this group were themselves feathered and show a close relationship to early birds such as *Archaeopteryx*. The first fossil occurrence of such dinosaurs and of *Archaeopteryx* was from late Jurassic times but the line leading to birds had probably diverged by the end of mid Jurassic times (Figure 4.2).

- Are birds more closely related to saurischian or to ornithischian dinosaurs (Figure 4.2)? Why is this something of a paradox?
- The saurischian dinosaurs, which have a reptile-like pelvis. The ornithischians have a bird-like pelvis (Box 4.1).

Perhaps surprisingly, the earliest bird, *Archaeopteryx*, had a saurischian pelvis and many other characters which ally it to saurischian dinosaurs such as troodontids and the dromaeosaurs (e.g. *Velociraptor*). Only later did the pelvis of early birds become like that of today's birds.

The remains of all sorts of land-living plants and animals, from insects to small dinosaurs (e.g. *Compsognathus*), were washed, or in some cases blown, into the Solenhofen lagoon to join the remains of the marine organisms which lived there in shallow depths, such as shrimps and the fish caught and eaten by some of the pterosaurs. A beautiful Solenhofen pterosaur, the type with a short tail called a pterodactyl, is shown on p.96 of the *Atlas*. The excellent preservation at Solenhofen is due to the lack of scavengers on the lagoon floor and the 'sealing in' of carcasses by sheets of microbes.

Now let's look in more detail at some of the invertebrates that thrived elsewhere in the Jurassic sea.

4.6 Life in the Jurassic sea

In this section we will look in detail at some of the invertebrate groups that thrived in the Jurassic sea. Firstly, Activity 4.1 focuses on ammonites, one of the most commonly found types of Jurassic fossil, indeed of the Mesozoic Era in general. In Section 4.6.1 we study some other fossil groups that can often be found in Jurassic strata.

Activity 4.1 The palaeobiology of ammonites

The estimated time for this activity is about 1.5 hours.

Aims

1 To examine and interpret the features of an ammonite replica, in order to understand aspects of the biology of this important extinct group.

2 To develop further the practical skills of observation and recording of information from fossils, using annotated diagrams.

Equipment

Kit items
Fossil replica C
Hand lens

Non-Kit items
Pencil, ruler, eraser

Practical procedure

Observations of fossil C

Fossil C, an ammonite, comes from very early Jurassic strata exposed in Robin Hood's Bay, Yorkshire. Examine the replica first with the naked eye, and then with the hand lens.

- Refer back to Box 3.1. To which phylum and class do ammonites belong, and to which era were they confined?

- Ammonites belong to the Phylum Mollusca and the Class Cephalopoda; they were confined to the Mesozoic.

- As they are cephalopods, in what general environment did the ammonites live?

- The sea. Cephalopods today are entirely marine, and they have been throughout their history (Box 3.1).

Ammonites were pelagic creatures (living above the sea floor), and like other cephalopods, most were nektonic, i.e. active swimmers (Section 3.1.2). They propelled themselves along by squirting out water, a form of jet propulsion. Like most other cephalopods many were probably predatory creatures, though some may have scavenged dead animals or trapped microscopic animals in the water.

- Look at the Wenlock Limestone scene on the title page. To which type of animals there do you think ammonites were most closely related?

- The squid-like animals with straight shells. These are a type of nautiloid.

- In Section 1.5 we saw that ammonites are particularly useful to geologists studying Mesozoic rocks. What is this use?

- They are used as zone fossils in the correlation of strata.

The shell of an ammonite is basically a coiled tube, divided across into many separate chambers. Each complete coil of the shell is called a **whorl**. The main body of the animal was housed in the outer, open end of the tube, called the **body chamber**. The body chamber varies in length; it tends to occupy between about half a whorl to one whole whorl. The living *Nautilus* (Figure 4.5) is useful for comparison; it is a cephalopod, which, rather like ammonites, also has a coiled shell divided into chambers. Its chambers are not visible in Figure 4.5, being inside the shell. The nautiloids, such as *Nautilus*, survived the mass extinction at the end of the Cretaceous (Section 4.11), unlike the ammonites. Ammonites were actually even more closely related to squid, cuttlefish and belemnites (see below) than to *Nautilus*.

Figure 4.5 A living *Nautilus*. The tentacles, eye and some other soft parts can be seen, as well as the shell. The chamber walls cannot be seen in this external view.

- Which general part of the *Nautilus* and ammonite shells do you think grew first, when the animals were very young?

- The inner whorls near the centre of their shells.

As the ammonite grew, it extended its tubular shell, and moved its body on outwards, laying down new chamber walls behind it. The earlier-formed chambers contained a mixture of gas and water by which the animal adjusted its buoyancy. The main ammonite body kept a connection with the earlier chambers by means of a thin tube extending from the body chamber right the way back to the first-formed chamber.

After an ammonite died, the chambers often became punctured and filled with sediment. In the case of this ammonite (the original is shown in Figure 4.6), the shell remained intact (unpunctured) so sediment could not seep into the chambers. The chambers were, however, filled with the mineral iron pyrites (fool's gold) as the shell lay surrounded by sediment a little below the sea floor. The pyrites formed in and around the rotting body by a chemical reaction between bacteria and seawater. Notice that the pyrites is, as is often the case, not very golden looking but a dark greenish brown. The boundary between light and dark parts of the body chamber is a weathering effect, not a biological feature.

Figure 4.6 The original ammonite specimen from the which the replica, fossil C, was made, to show the nature of its preservation.

The chamber walls of ammonites are highly complex in shape. Where each wall joins the tubular part of the shell it shows up as highly intricate frilled pattern, but this is only visible if the tubular outer wall of the shell has been dissolved away (as is the case in fossil C), or if it has peeled off. Look at fossil C with the hand lens; you should be able to see these frilled patterns, called **sutures**, crossing the shell. Each suture looks a bit like the intricate margin of a leaf, such as that of a fern. The chamber wall itself was very thin — the thickness of the suture line itself (less than 0.5 mm).

The shape of the sutures, like the shape of the shell, is important in the classification of ammonites. Ammonites had a much more complex suture than nautiloids, such as *Nautilus*, which has a gentle curving suture (see Figure 4.7 and the cover of this book, which shows a modern *Nautilus* shell cut across to reveal the chambers). The primary function of the highly complex ammonite chamber wall was probably to provide strength. Ammonite shells are always thinner than those of nautiloids, and the complex frilled pattern almost certainly acted as a sort of buttressing of the main tube of the shell, preventing it from collapsing inwards from the pressure at depth in the sea. Figure 4.8 (overleaf) shows another species of Jurassic ammonite with many sutures visible, though the body chamber is clearly missing. Note that the end-on view in Figure 4.8 reveals the shape of a single chamber wall. It is relatively smooth in the more central area but becomes very folded as it approaches the outside, where the shell of the main tube would be, had it not been dissolved away.

Figure 4.7 A Jurassic nautiloid, *Cenoceras inornatum* (8 cm). The typically simple, gently curving sutures can be seen in this internal mould (the shell has dissolved away). Note that the body chamber is missing.

- How far back along the inner whorls towards the central, first-formed part of the shell can you see the sutures in fossil C? Use your hand lens. To see the sutures clearly, you may need to tilt the replica so that light is shining obliquely across it.

- The sutures can be detected right back almost to the centre, though not the innermost couple of whorls (although the sutures were there too).

(a)

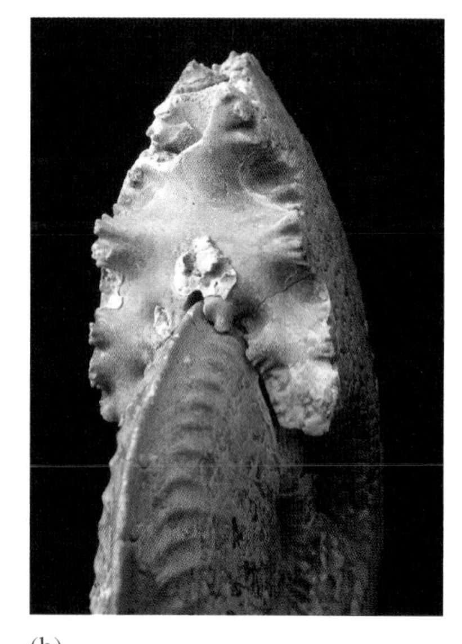

(b)

Figure 4.8 The Jurassic ammonite *Amoeboceras serratum*: (a) side view (10 cm); (b) end-on view of outermost whorl (field of view 6 cm). See text for discussion.

To find where the body chamber begins in fossil C, examine the shell as it spirals outwards and eventually the sutures stop, and you don't find another one where you would expect it from their previous spacing. In this fossil, the body chamber is present (as an internal mould; Section 1.2), although in many ammonite specimens extracted or washed out from the rock the body chamber is missing. Having an open end, the body chamber is easily crushed and so is difficult to collect. In this specimen, the sediment that filled the body chamber, and the sediment around the shell, became hardened due to the addition of natural mineral cements, and this prevented the body chamber from being crushed by the weight of sediment which accumulated on top of it.

To help you understand these aspects of preservation, look for a moment at the ammonite in Figure 4.9. Its appearance is very different. Why? Here the chambers did not get filled with hard minerals at an early stage as the shell lay within the sediment, and the whole shell became crushed under the weight of overlying strata, leaving a fossil only about a millimetre or so thick. Unlike in fossil C, the shell of this specimen has not been dissolved away. The original shell material, made of the calcium carbonate mineral aragonite, still remains; it has a typical pinkish mother-of-pearl appearance. Note that no sutures are visible; they are covered over by the shell.

The shell of fossil C has a conspicuous series of ridges, called **ribs**, each far simpler in shape than that of a chamber wall. They are clearly visible on internal moulds (such as this) as well as on the original shell viewed from the outside. The main function of the ribs is not certain; they may have strengthened the shell. The ribs are completely unrelated to the sutures.

Question 4.2 Using a ruler, estimate the average distance between (a) sutures and (b) ribs in the vicinity of the last-formed sutures. Make your measurements on the periphery (outer edge) of the specimen, looking along the plane of the shell. ◀

- In many ammonite species, one can tell if the individual ammonite was an adult because the last-formed chambers were shorter, causing the sutures to become bunched together. Is this the case with this specimen?
- There is some variation but no clear bunching up of the sutures.
- Can you think of how, if you had time and opportunity, you would go about testing to see if this individual was a juvenile, i.e. not an adult, when it died?
- You could attempt to find other, larger specimens of the species and observe whether or not their last-formed sutures became bunched up. If they did, especially if they did consistently at a size larger than this specimen, then you could conclude that this one was not an adult.

The photo of the replica in Figure 4.10 is orientated so that the body chamber is at the bottom, as it would have been in the life of the animal (as in *Nautilus*, Figure 4.5).

Now label on Figure 4.10 these parts: *start of body chamber*; *internal mould of body chamber*; *suture (edge of chamber wall)*; *rib*; *first-formed part of shell*; *outermost whorl*. Draw a scale bar to indicate the extent of a centimetre on the specimen. Write in the name of this species: *Aegasteroceras sagittarium*. Remember to underline it.

To check your completed Figure 4.10, compare it with Figure 4.29 (in the 'Comments on activities' section at the end of the book).

The ammonite shell has a single plane of symmetry that divides the shell into two equal parts. Just over one half of the ammonite shell is visible on the replica; almost all the other half — the mirror image on the other side of the plane of symmetry — lies (in effect) in the base of the replica.

Question 4.3 Estimate the approximate total maximum width of the shell (in mm), measured at right-angles to the plane of symmetry across the last-formed part of the body chamber. ◀

Ammonite shell shapes varied greatly, and so probably did their lifestyles. Those with fatter profiles in cross-section would have presented a greater resistance to motion in the water and were probably quite sluggish; sleek ones were probably adapted for faster motion, though experimental studies with models show they could achieve only a fraction of the speed of today's squid. Some ammonite groups, especially in the later part of the Cretaceous, evolved rather bizarre shapes. Some species became uncoiled during growth and then coiled up again at the end; others formed an unlikely tangle of U-shaped bends. In yet others the shell coiled in a screw-like spiral like a gastropod (snail) shell (Section 4.10.1), though being an ammonite the shell had chambers, unlike gastropods. These forms were specialized to particular niches; there is no reason to think they were any less adapted to their environment than those with more normal coiling patterns. ◀

Figure 4.9 The early Jurassic ammonite *Psiloceras planorbis* (5.5 cm). See text for discussion of its preservation.

Figure 4.10 Plan view of a replica of fossil C.

4.6.1 Some other invertebrates in the Jurassic sea

First, let's look at another group of cephalopods that are common fossils in Jurassic rocks.

Belemnites

The word 'belemnite' comes from the Greek for 'dart', and looking again at Figure 4.4b it is easy to see the reason for this name. These distinctive fossils are the internal skeleton of an extinct group whose closest relatives today include squid, cuttlefish and octopuses. Like the ammonites, belemnites became extinct at the end of the Cretaceous (Section 4.11).

Figure 4.11 shows a reconstruction of a typical living belemnite. The part of the belemnite usually preserved is a solid piece of calcite called the **guard**. At the front of the guard is a chambered shell, which in some ways resembles a straightened-out, cone-shaped ammonite shell. Figure 4.12 shows a belemnite split down the middle to reveal this cone-shaped chambered shell, called the **phragmocone**. The chamber walls are not complex like those of an ammonite, and can be seen running straight across the shell. Often the phragmocone falls out, leaving a cone-shaped hollow, as can be seen at the top of the broken specimen in Figure 4.4b. In cross-section, belemnite guards have a very distinctive structure of fine, shiny fibres of calcite radiating out from the centre; it is these fibres that readily distinguish belemnites from other cylindrical fossils such as burrows or crinoid stems. Belemnites are often found in Jurassic and Cretaceous clays, from which they easily get washed out. Because they are so robust, belemnite guards, or at least fragments of them, often get derived into gravels, as do the thick fossil oyster shells (see below) with which they often occur in Jurassic strata. Sometimes belemnite fossils occur together in large numbers, so-called 'belemnite battlefields', that in some cases represent mass mortality after mating, as in modern squid.

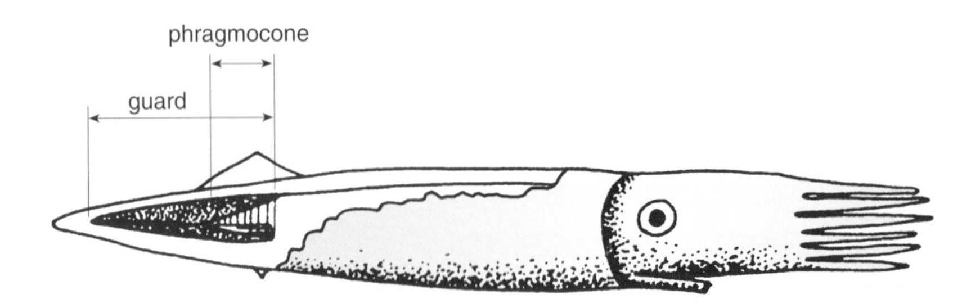

Figure 4.11 Reconstruction of a living belemnite. The soft tissue is shown as if partially removed to reveal the internal skeleton at the rear.

Figure 4.12 A belemnite split down the middle to reveal the cone-shaped, chambered phragmocone. Width of belemnite 3 cm.

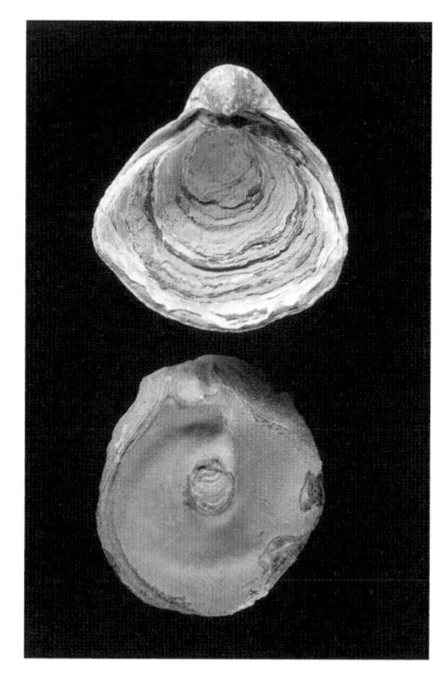

Figure 4.13 The Jurassic oyster, *Gryphaea dilatata* (8 cm). (Above) a complete shell; (below) internal view of a detached upper valve, showing the single, almost central, muscle scar.

Note that these hard parts were entirely covered by soft tissue, and thus they formed an internal skeleton. The cuttlefish 'bone' (which budgerigars are often given to nibble) is similarly an internal skeleton. Although cuttlefish are related to belemnites, their 'bone' structure, a modified phragmocone, is rather different from that of a belemnite.

- What proportion of the whole belemnite animal in Figure 4.11 does the belemnite guard represent?

- Only about a fifth. So if you find a belemnite, remember that the whole animal was considerably bigger.

Belemnites probably swam like squids, with the guard acting as a counterweight to the head end of the animal, keeping the body level when in motion.

Bivalves

As we saw in Section 1.4, most bivalve molluscs have a shell with two valves of equal size and shape, one a mirror image of the other. In a few groups, however, such as oysters, this is not so. Look again at Figure 4.4a, which shows a type of oyster nicknamed the 'Devil's toenail'; it is common in Jurassic shallow-water clays and muddy limestones. One valve is much bigger than the other. In early life, when very small, the shell was cemented to the sea floor. As it grew heavier, it rolled over and lay with the larger, thicker valve partly anchored in the mud. The animal could raise its hinged, lid-like upper valve for feeding, respiration and so on, and lower it for protection of the soft parts inside. Figure 4.13 shows another species of the genus *Gryphaea* in which selection had favoured a more stable, broader and flatter shell like many modern oysters. Note the conspicuous **growth lines**, parallel to the margin, that represent edges of the shell at successive stages in its life, and so record its growth history.

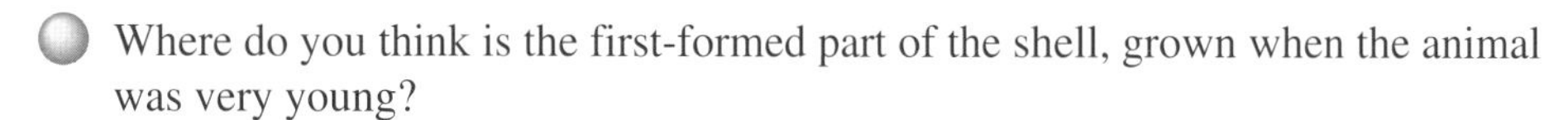

- Where do you think is the first-formed part of the shell, grown when the animal was very young?

- It is where all the growth lines meet, near the apex of the shell.

Oysters have one muscle to close the shell, unlike cockles, for example, which have two (Section 1.4). The scar of this single, now almost central muscle (the edible part of modern oysters) is often clearly visible on the inner surface of isolated valves (Figure 4.13).

Some other Jurassic bivalves are pictured in Figure 4.14. *Pholadomya* and *Trigonia* have the more usual bivalve symmetry (one valve being the mirror image of the other).

(a)

(b)

Figure 4.14 Two marine bivalves common in the Jurassic. (a) *Pholadomya fidicula* (5 cm); (b) *Trigonia costata* (6.5 cm).

Figure 4.15 Internal mould of the late Jurassic gastropod, *Aptyxiella portlandica* (7 cm).

Gastropods

Although gastropods (Box 3.1) are generally not so common as bivalves in the Jurassic, they are often locally abundant. Figure 4.15 shows an internal mould (Section 1.2) of a marine gastropod species so locally abundant in Portland Stone, a late Jurassic limestone, that it is known as 'the Portland Screw'. The shell itself, which was made of aragonite (Section 3.4), had a tendency to dissolve away, as here. Remember that gastropods, like bivalves, are not necessarily marine, though the majority are.

Brachiopods

Brachiopods are common in the Jurassic, especially in limestones; Figure 4.16 shows two types. Note that, unlike in bivalves (molluscs), the plane of symmetry in brachiopods passes *through* both valves, rather than between them, and one valve is generally larger than the other (Box 3.1).

- Which part of the body is indicated by the presence of the hole in the larger valve, as can clearly be seen in *Epithyris oxonica* (Figure 4.16a)?

- The stalk (pedicle) by which the brachiopod was attached to the sea floor (Box 3.1).

The pedicle was attached to a rock or shell fragment, and enabled the shell to swivel with the current. The shell hinged open and shut along the junction between the two valves, quite near the hole for the pedicle. Note that, as in bivalves, it may be possible to detect growth lines. These are most conspicuous when there was a change in growth rate, and examples of the latter can be seen in *Epithyris* (Figure 4.16a). The fact that they are towards the edge of the shell means that these fluctuations in growth rate were produced relatively late in life. These more or less concentric growth lines are quite different structures from the ridges or **ribs** that, in some brachiopods, such as *Tetrarhynchia* (Figure 4.16b), radiate out across the shell from the point of first growth.

Figure 4.16 Two Jurassic brachiopods: (a) *Epithyris oxonica* (4 cm); (b) *Tetrarhynchia tetrahedra* (2.5 cm).

4.7 The Cretaceous Period

Let's now put the late Mesozoic world in better perspective. The supercontinent of Pangea began to break up in Jurassic times, an important aspect of which was the formation of the Atlantic Ocean. A good impression of what happened to the continents as the Atlantic opened can be gained in the following way. Turn to p.31 of the *Atlas* and look in the top right-hand corner labelled 'Whole world projection'. Now, keeping your eyes on that top right area, turn over the next nine pages, taking you rapidly through the last 240 million years up to the present day. Fixing your gaze on the area between South America and Africa, and North America and Europe, notice how the Atlantic opens up, i.e. starts to widen, first in the middle (where it is widest today), then in the south, and finally, from early Tertiary times, in the north. You can read more about this process of ocean formation in the *Atlas*, pp.174–175 if you wish.

Question 4.4 Look at the plot of changes in global sea level through time shown on p.91 of the *Atlas*. To what extent is the pattern of sea-level change in the Cretaceous similar to that in the Jurassic, and during which of these two periods was sea level higher, on average? ◀

Now read the *Atlas*, pp.108–109.

Although the *Atlas* (p.108) suggests that the melting of ice caps was a major cause of sea-level rise in the early Cretaceous, in fact this influence was probably quite minor as the ice caps remained small throughout the Mesozoic. Much more important seems to have been large-scale doming of parts of the Pacific ocean floor due to mantle plumes, i.e. magma rising from deep in the mantle (*Atlas G*, p.211), together with an increased rate of sea-floor spreading, producing broad mid-ocean ridges that displaced large volumes of water. The flooding of large areas of continental shelves with shallow seas promoted an increase in marine diversity, with the evolution of many new fish and invertebrate families.

Not surprisingly, as the Atlantic Ocean developed, the separation of continents, the creation of new seaways, and the change of latitudes all had a major influence on the evolution of life, both on land and in the sea. For example, when the land link that allowed the migration of dinosaurs between Europe and North America was broken, the ornithopod dinosaurs went their separate ways: in North America large hypsilophodonts became dominant, whilst in Europe the iguanodonts continued to thrive.

4.8 Cretaceous life

4.8.1 The discovery of dinosaurs and the world of *Iguanodon*

Read the *Atlas*, pp.110–111 and p.112.

In the early nineteenth century, the strata of southeast England were revealing completely new types of fossils, some of which did not fit any then known groups of animals, living or extinct. Most spectacular amongst these were some large bones and strange teeth uncovered by quarrymen in Sussex. They were studied by Gideon Mantell, a practising doctor and amateur geologist who spent as much time as he could investigating the fossils of strange creatures emerging from his local rocks.

Mantell was able to compare the odd, somewhat leaf-shaped fossil teeth (Figure 4.17) with those of the living iguana (see photo on *Atlas*, p.112), a specimen of which had arrived in London in 1824 from Barbados. The similarities were so remarkable that Mantell named his fossil *Iguanodon* in 1825. The main difference was the much greater size of the fossil teeth and bones, which Mantell compared with their counterparts in the iguana and found them to be between ten and twenty times bigger. For example, Mantell measured the length of the iguana shoulder blade at 1.5 inches, whereas the length of the shoulder blade of *Iguanodon* was 30 inches, 20 times bigger. Then, by simple linear scaling up from the 5-foot iguana, Mantell calculated that his fossil monster might have been 100 feet long. This was far bigger than any known living land animal: ancient monsters were no longer mythical.

Figure 4.17 A tooth of the dinosaur *Iguanodon*. The tooth is 4.5 cm long. Despite the steak-knife-like serrations on its edges, *Iguanodon* was a plant eater.

But Mantell was wrong. *Iguanodon* was no more than 30 feet long (9 m): only the largest of the giant sauropods reached lengths of 100 feet (30 m). Part of the problem was that simple linear scaling can rarely be applied to animals in this way. But the other problem for Mantell and other naturalists studying such incomplete fossils was how to reconstruct their skeletons and what model to use. Amongst living reptiles the most obvious analogues (i.e. animals on which to model a reconstruction) were lizards, such as the iguana, and crocodiles. Mantell used a lizard model and his reconstructed *Iguanodon* was inevitably too long (see his sketch, *Atlas*, p.112). Only much later in the nineteenth century, when complete skeletons of *Iguanodon* were discovered in Belgium, did it become clear that living lizards were not appropriate models. By this time, the name 'dinosaur' had been coined by Mantell's rival, Richard Owen, in 1842 (*Atlas*, pp.113, 183 and 191); his version of *Iguanodon* is shown on p.183 of the *Atlas*.

- What modern animals were used as models by Dollo and De Pauw to reconstruct the Belgian *Iguanodon* skeletons found in 1878, and why?

- An emu and a kangaroo. The structure of the hip and hind legs appears distinctly bird-like, whereas unlike birds, *Iguanodon* also had a long muscular tail, strong forearms, wrists and hands, which were thought to be kangaroo-like (*Atlas*, p.110).

This was a good try but there are problems with the Dollo–De Pauw reconstruction. Although *Iguanodon*'s forelimbs are shorter than its hind limbs, they are nevertheless very powerful, with strong wrists and weight-bearing hands, suggesting that they could have been used for walking. Also, bone-like (ossified) ligaments joined the tail bones together to make the tail stiff; it could not have been flexed like a kangaroo's tail. The stiff, heavy tail of *Iguanodon* was used as a counterbalance to the mass of the animal's head, neck and torso, as shown in the current reconstruction of *Iguanodon* on p.111 of the *Atlas*.

Living alongside *Iguanodon* was another ornithischian, the 1.5 m long *Hypsilophodon*. When *Hysilophodon* was first described by Thomas Henry Huxley in 1870, he thought that it might have been able to perch and climb trees like the living tree kangaroo. Subsequently, as with *Iguanodon*, it was realized that the long muscular tail was held quite stiffly in a subhorizontal position and acted as a counterbalance to the weight of the head and torso (see reconstruction, *Atlas*, p.110).

- What is the present interpretation of *Hypsilophodon*'s mode of life?

- It was a gazelle-like herbivore, built for speed and agility (*Atlas*, p.111).

If this interpretation is correct, such animals would have needed high metabolic rates to sustain such energy demands, and required a high-energy, specialized plant diet.

With hindsight, we can see why it was so difficult for Mantell, Owen, and the other early naturalists to reconstruct these 'alien beasts' from the deep past. Above all, they simply did not have appropriate living analogues — a common problem for palaeontologists dealing with extinct groups.

4.8.2 Cretaceous Park

Thanks to science fiction writer Michael Crichton and film-maker Steven Spielberg, the Jurassic Period is popularly considered as the heyday of the dinosaurs. However, as we saw earlier (Section 4.2), the greatest diversity of major dinosaur groups was attained in Cretaceous times; the infamous tyrannosaurs, for example, date from this period.

It will help to have a brief overview of the main dinosaur groups in the Cretaceous before you read more pages of the *Atlas*. The page numbers in brackets after dinosaur genera refer to illustrations given in the *Atlas*. Remember that Figure 4.2 is a useful summary.

Let's first look at saurischians in the Cretaceous. Among these were two groups of mainly predatory theropods (Figure 4.2). One group ranged through from the Jurassic and contained the large predatory **megalosaurs** and **allosaurs**. The taxonomy of megalosaurs is being revised, and the form labelled *Megalosaurus* (*Atlas*, p.110) is now referred to the allosaur *Neovenator*. *Megalosaurus* is now regarded as mainly if not exclusively Jurassic. The other, rather mixed, group contained mainly predators which ranged in size from the infamous giant flesh-eating **tyrannosaurs** (*Atlas G*, p.215) such as *Tarbosaurus* (*Atlas*, p.116), *Tyrannosaurus* (p.114), *Daspletosaurus* (p.119) and *Albertosaurus* (p.124) to much smaller forms. Amongst these smaller theropods were the strange, toothless **oviraptors**, e.g. *Oviraptor* (p.117); the fleet-footed, bipedal predatory **dromaeosaurs** (*Atlas G*, p.207) with slashing claws, e.g. *Velociraptor* (*Atlas*, pp.114, 117); the possibly plant-eating, ostrich-like **ornithomimids**, e.g. *Gallimimus* (p.116); and **troodontids**, e.g. the bird-like *Troodon* (p.118). Some of these had an exceptionally large brain for their body size, and were probably as intelligent as modern birds. A variety of quadrupedal, plant-eating sauropods were also present in the Cretaceous.

Now to ornithischians, which diversified greatly in Cretaceous times, especially in the late Cretaceous, when some spread globally.

- Look at Figure 4.2. Which three groups of ornithischians existed only or mainly in the late Cretaceous? Were they carnivores or herbivores?

- The hadrosaurids, pachycephalosaurids and ceratopsians. They were herbivores, like all ornithischians (Box 4.1).

Let's consider these three groups of ornithischians in turn. **Hadrosaurs** (*Atlas G*, p.209), the 'duck-billed dinosaurs', were common bipedal plant eaters with duck-like beaks and webbed feet. Many hadrosaurs were 10 m or so long and weighed over 10 tonnes when fully grown. Examples are *Maiasaura* (*Atlas*, pp.115, 119), *Parasaurolophus* (pp.118, 125), *Corythosaurus* (p.119), *Lambeosaurus* (p.125) and *Edmontosaurus* (p.125). Apart from their size, hadrosaurs had little in the way of defensive structures for protection against large predators. Like many large plant-eating mammals today, they may well have relied mainly on herding behaviour and highly developed sense organs for protection. Indeed, some hadrosaurs, such as *Parasaurolophus* and *Lambeosaurus* had strange hollow crests on the top of their skulls which were extensions of their nasal passages. These are thought to have been used to produce a cacophony of snorts, honks, whistles and hoots — an in-built brass band for communication between members of the herd, including warnings of danger.

The **pachycephalosaurids**, such as the 4.6 m long *Pachycephalosaurus* (*Atlas*, p.118), were a mainly late Cretaceous group of small to medium-sized, bipedal plant eaters. These 'thick-headed dinosaurs' were characterized by enormously thickened skulls thought to have been used for 'head-butting' opponents.

The **ceratopsians** (*Atlas G*, p.206) included the 2.5 m long *Protoceratops* (*Atlas*, p.117) from Mongolia, with its distinctive neck frill at the back of its head, and beaked jaws; another Mongolian form was *Psittacosaurus* (p.109). North American landscapes were populated by other ceratopsians, such as *Styracosaurus* (p.118) and *Chasmosaurus* (p.122), both about 5 m long, and the spectacular *Triceratops* (pp.124, 128), 9 m long.

As Figure 4.2 shows, two other ornithischian groups persisted into the Cretaceous from the Jurassic — the **ankylosaurs** (*Atlas G*, p.204) and the **stegosaurs** (*Atlas G*, p.214). Ankylosaurs survived right up to the end of the Cretaceous. The 6 m long *Euoplocephalus* (*Atlas*, pp.118–119), the 4 m long *Polacanthus* (p.110) and the 10 m long *Ankylosaurus* (p.125) were armoured a bit like mediaeval knights, with heavy plates or spikes of bone covering the body. In some genera the tail ended in a massive bony club. The stegosaurs (see *Atlas*, pp.99, 113 for Jurassic ones) were four-legged, medium-sized plant eaters with a double row of large bony plates protecting their backbone, and a tail with bony spikes. Curiously, there is no evidence that the back plates were attached to the backbone; they may have lain flat on the animal's back, rather than standing upright as most reconstructions show. They could also have been used as heat exchangers, as the plates were probably covered in thick, leathery skin and blood vessels.

We met two other groups of ornithischian dinosaurs, each primarily Cretaceous, in Section 4.8.1 — the **iguanodontids**, e.g. *Iguanodon* (*Atlas*, p.111), and the **hypsilophodontids** (Figure 4.2). The hypsilophodontids (*Atlas G*, p.210) spread over wide areas of Europe and North America and were somewhat similar to hadrosaurs in their habits. Most were small with long slender legs, such as *Hypsilophodon* (*Atlas*, p.110).

The term **ornithopods** (*Atlas G*, p.212) is used for ornithischian dinosaurs that predominantly walked on their hind limbs and had feet with three main toes. This big grouping includes: iguanodontids, hypsilophodontids, hadrosaurids, and the early Jurassic heterodontosaurids (Figure 4.2). Ornithopods were unique among reptiles in being able to chew their food (as can mammals); other reptiles just gulp(ed) it down.

The most diverse dinosaur fauna in Europe is found in early Cretaceous rocks of the Isle of Wight, southern England. Here ornithopods including *Iguanodon* and *Hypsilophodon* occur along with sauropods, an ankylosaur, an allosaur, and other groups. A new museum called 'Dinosaur Isle' on the beach at Sandown displays these finds.

We will consider the extinction of the dinosaurs shortly in Section 4.11.

Now read the *Atlas*, pp.114–119. Remember — don't get too bogged down with all the names that are mentioned.

In the hope of finding ever bigger and 'meaner' dinosaurs, there has been intense searching of Cretaceous terrestrial (land-based) deposits, especially in North America (*Atlas*, pp.118–119) and Mongolia (pp.116–117). Recently, however, these regions have yielded many less spectacular but scientifically important finds of early mammals (p.117).

Other terrestrial groups that become increasingly important in the Cretaceous were the early flowering plants (angiosperms, Section 4.9), insects and birds.

- The evolution of flowering plants and insects has often been closely connected, with adaptations in species of both groups evolving in concert (coevolution). Why is this?

- Many flowering plants depend on insects to assist in cross-pollination, with the insects benefiting from flower nectar as food.

Most of the Cretaceous birds were carnivores, ranging from sparrow-sized, insect eaters to fish-eating birds over a metre in size. There were also some strange flightless birds and bird-like dinosaurs, such as *Mononykus* (see illustration, *Atlas*, p.116); experts are divided about whether some are dinosaurs or birds.

Question 4.5 Check the following statements and correct any errors. (a) *Oviraptor*, the 'egg stealer', is believed to have eaten the eggs of *Protoceratops*, in whose nest it was found. (b) In late Cretaceous times, the most abundant mammals were the insect-eating marsupials and monotremes. (c) *Tyrannosaurus rex* belonged to the largest group of theropod dinosaurs, the tyrannosaurids. It could almost certainly run at 30 miles per hour chasing the live prey that always formed its diet. ◀

4.8.3 Cretaceous Marina

Cretaceous seas were perhaps more dangerous than at any other time. Large predators ranged from sharks to ichthyosaurs (Section 4.3), plesiosaurs (Section 4.3), marine crocodiles and mosasaurs.

Now read the *Atlas*, pp.120–121.

Question 4.6 Correct the errors in the following passage about mosasaurs, perhaps the most awesome marine predators ever to have lived.

'The mosasaurs evolved from a group of marine snakes in the late Jurassic. They were mainly propelled through the water by their paddle-like limbs. After thriving for 70 million years, they became extinct 80 million years ago, and their niche in the world's oceans was soon taken up by the ichthyosaurs in the early Cenozoic Era.' ◀

In Section 4.10 we will look at some marine invertebrates which, though not as spectacular as the vertebrates discussed above, are nevertheless far more common as fossils. First, though, we'll consider a major evolutionary event that was eventually to affect a large proportion of all life on land — the origin of flowering plants.

4.9 Flowering plants and their origins

Read the section headed 'flowering plants' on pp.136–137 of the *Atlas*.

Today's land vegetation is characterized by the flowering plants or angiosperms. Figure 3.15 shows that angiosperms are the most recent major group of plants to have evolved, and yet they have become highly diverse in a relatively short time. It is difficult to say exactly when or how the angiosperms arose, but before the mid Cretaceous they were not ecologically important and made up a tiny proportion of the terrestrial biomass. In mid Cretaceous time, pollen, leaves, and wood that clearly look angiospermous, and even flowers themselves, became increasingly common. During the late Cretaceous, flowering plants with combinations of features that characterize many modern families became numerous, if not dominant, in many environments, particularly in frequently disturbed settings such as river margins. Today, angiosperms are both numerous and extremely diverse: there are about 250 000 species belonging to approximately 450 families, and almost all our food crops are angiosperms.

To understand the evolutionary history of angiosperms we have to rely on robust, decay-resistant morphological characters that tend to be preserved in the fossil record. So what can be used to define an angiosperm in fossil material? There are several such features, but not all angiosperms have them all, and some non-angiosperms have some of them.

Look at the reconstruction of the Swedish late Cretaceous flower with red petals on p.137 of the *Atlas*. This is similar to a typical flower today, revealing that many of the key features of angiosperms were present quite early in the group's evolution. A typical flower is made up of a ring of scale-like **sepals** surrounding a ring of brightly coloured **petals**. Within the petal ring (known as a **corolla**), whose function it is to attract insects, there is a ring of male pollen-producing organs (commonly called **stamens**). The most internal structure is the central, female part of the flower with the **ovaries** containing the potential seeds. From the ovary protrudes a stalk-like **style** and on this is the pollen-receiving surface, the **stigma**. From this you can see that such a flower is bisexual (i.e. it has both male and female parts). The potential seeds or **ovules** are enclosed and pollen is received on a special stigmatic surface because the grains do not have direct access to the enclosed ovules.

Angiosperms were not unique in having flower structures with bisexual reproductive organs: they are also found, for example, in the extinct cycad-like bennettitales in the mid Jurassic (Section 3.7). So if flowers don't define an angiosperm, what does? Let's look at the possibilities.

Angiosperm leaves tend to be quite different from those of ferns, cycadophytes and conifers (Section 3.7). They usually have a network of veins that divide and reconnect many times. This reticulate venation is, however, not unique to angiosperms: the modern non-angiospermous *Gnetum* (pronounced 'nee-tum') and Jurassic seed ferns also have reticulate leaves. Moreover, some angiosperms such as palms and grasses have parallel veins rather than a network.

The wood of many modern angiosperms is characterized by having water-conducting vessels in addition to the other types of cells that are also found in conifers. In cross-section, these vessels can be quite large and may be either organized in a diffuse pattern or grouped mostly in the 'early wood' produced early in the growing season (Figure 4.18). Although most modern angiosperms have vessels, some do not. Cretaceous fossils indicate that there were several evolutionary routes to vessel formation, and that some groups which today possess vessels probably did not in the past. Moreover, some non-angiosperms, such as the Gnetales, also have vessels. Vessels, therefore, are not uniquely diagnostic of flowering plants.

Several other features are commonly found in angiosperms, but none is *exclusive* to them, nor are they found in all angiosperms, nor do they tend to fossilize. There is, however, one preservable feature, at the core of the concept of angiospermy, which has recently been used to rewrite the early history of angiosperms — the enclosure of the ovules by an outer covering to form a **carpel**.

Ovules (unfertilized seeds) are attractive to animals because they are very nutritious, even though in some angiosperms they contain little in the way of food reserves for the developing plant embryo. Enclosing the ovules in a carpel affords extra protection against predators. More importantly perhaps, the fertilization process itself takes place in a controlled environment within the carpel wall, so angiosperms, unlike more primitive plants such as ferns, are not restricted by the external environment during this critical phase of the life cycle.

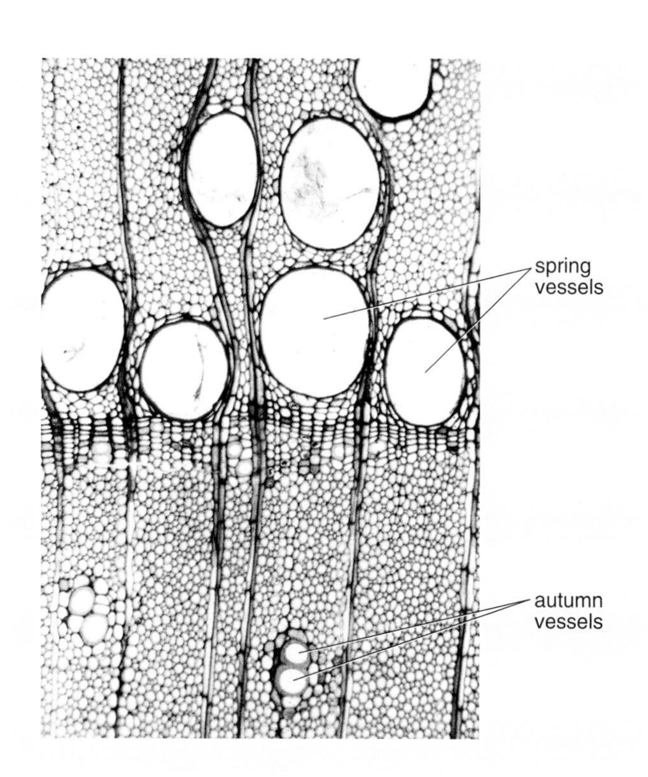

Figure 4.18 Cross-section of an annual ring from a piece of modern angiosperm wood (oak), showing the large water-conducting vessels. In this species the vessels produced in the spring, when leaves are growing and demand for water is high, are larger than those produced in the autumn, when the leaves are beginning to die. The field of view is about 1 mm.

Although building an extra wall around the ovules required extra resources, such an evolutionary innovation clearly has advantages, and a trend towards ovule enclosure occurred in several lines of Mesozoic plants. Partial enclosure is seen in some cycadophytes, some glossopterids, and in particular the seed fern *Caytonia*, named after Cayton Bay near Scarborough, Yorkshire, where it was first found. The partially enclosed ovules of *Caytonia* and its reticulate venation led early researchers to suggest it was an angiosperm. We now know, however, that enclosure of the ovules so as to require a stigmatic surface for pollen germination was not present in *Caytonia*.

The first convincing evidence of the evolution of a true carpel currently comes from the early Cretaceous of China. On p.137 of the *Atlas* you will see a photograph of *Archaefructus*. This fossil consists of a specialized reproductive branch with helically arranged fruits. The simplest way to envisage these fruits is to think of a leaf with two to four ovules attached along the midrib (the main central vein), and the leaf folded along the midrib so that the leaf margins meet and enclose the ovules completely. This structure meets the criterion required for it to be considered a carpel. No corolla or male reproductive parts are known, nor are normal leaves, but these fruit-bearing branches are associated with leaf-like structures, as yet poorly known.

Is *Archaefructus* a true angiosperm? It does appear to be if we define angiospermy purely on the enclosure of the ovules. However, even in the modern angiosperm *Drimys* enclosure of the ovules is not complete at fertilization. Other features that could, if taken together, indicate that *Archaefructus* was an angiosperm are lacking.

Is *Archaefructus* the ancestor of modern flowering plants? This question is even more difficult to answer. The evolutionary tendency for enclosure of ovules was widespread in Mesozoic times, as was the evolution of reticulate leaf venation, and bisexual reproductive structures. Clearly, Mesozoic environmental conditions favoured features that we now see as characteristic of flowering plants. At some point in time, probably the late Jurassic or early Cretaceous, these features appeared together within a single group of plants, allowing the possessors to outperform many competitors. As a consequence, the angiosperms underwent a rapid geographic spread, and by the mid Cretaceous they were ecologically significant in many environments from pole to pole.

4.10 Life in the late Cretaceous Chalk sea

In this section we will look in detail at some of the marine organisms that flourished in the late Cretaceous. The third and final Activity using the Kit replicas focuses on sea urchins, and in Section 4.10.1 we look at a range of other groups commonly found in the Chalk. The term 'Chalk', with a capital C, refers specifically to late Cretaceous deposits of fine-grained, white limestone made up mostly of coccoliths. **Coccoliths** are minute calcite plates that belonged to phytoplankton which floated abundantly in the late Cretaceous sea (see also *Atlas*, p.173 under 'shallow seas'). We will meet coccoliths again in Section 4.11. These plates accumulated in countless billions on the sea bed, which was most of the time free from strong currents that would have moved the fine sediment elsewhere. Later, the water between the coccoliths and other organic remains was squeezed out, and the sediment became a rock. Next time you pick up a piece of Chalk, you will be holding a vast number of fossils, though this is far from apparent: coccoliths are so small that not until the invention of the scanning electron microscope was it possible to establish what formed the bulk of the Chalk. Incidentally, blackboard 'chalk' is not the same: it is mostly the soft mineral gypsum (calcium sulphate).

The Chalk is a widespread deposit found in southern and eastern England, northern Ireland, northern France, elsewhere across northern Europe, and also in North America and Australia. Sea levels were high: Figure 4.19 shows the great extent of sea across the British Isles in the late Cretaceous. The English Chalk was probably deposited between 50 m and 200 m in depth. Much of the Chalk originally deposited has now been eroded away. Some of the typical eroding Chalk cliffs of southern England are shown on p.108 of the *Atlas*.

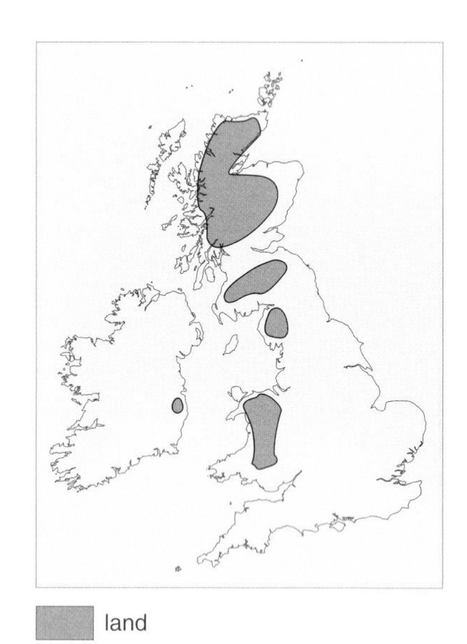

Figure 4.19 Map showing the extent of sea across the British Isles in the late Cretaceous, about 75 Ma ago.

Activity 4.2 Sea urchins from the Chalk sea

The estimated time for this Activity is about 1.5 hours.

Aims

1 To examine and interpret the features of a fossil sea urchin replica, in order to understand aspects of the biology of this important group.

2 To develop further the practical skills of observation and recording of information from fossils, using annotated drawings.

Equipment

Kit items

Fossil replica D

Hand lens

Non-Kit items

Pencil, ruler, eraser

Practical procedure

Examine fossil D first with the naked eye, and then with the hand lens. View it from different angles to ensure you get a feel for its three-dimensional form. Oblique lighting will show up the details best.

Note: You may notice the replica has a number of little round holes in some places, especially on small raised structures that elsewhere lack such holes; if so, these are gas bubbles trapped in the making of the replica — please ignore them.

Having already read the description of echinoderms in Section 1.4, and seen Figures 1.12 and 1.13, you should not have had too much trouble recognizing this fossil as a sea urchin (echinoid). (If you did, read that part of Section 1.4 again.)

- To which of the other three Kit fossils is this sea urchin most closely related?

- The crinoid (fossil B), which being an echinoderm, belongs to the same phylum.

This particular sea urchin species is remarkable for having massive, club-shaped spines, many of which remain in place in this specimen. The large spines were attached to knobs arranged in five paired rows radiating from the centre. Check this now — you should be able to count ten radial rows of large knobs or spines.

The sea urchin skeleton is called a **test**. Although the test is made up of many calcite plates, the boundaries between individual plates are hard or impossible to discern in this case, so don't worry that you can't see them. In live sea urchins, the plates are covered by a very thin skin.

- What are the soft, multipurpose organs that a sea urchin uses for feeding, respiration, locomotion and, in some species, constructing burrows?

- Tube feet (Section 1.4).

The tube feet projected through little paired pores in the plates of the test. These plates bearing tube feet are located in five, relatively narrow, radial zones between the double rows of plates with large knobs and spines. See if you can locate these five radial zones. Don't worry if you can't detect the pores themselves — they are in tiny grooves and rather hard to see. The pore pairs are in two columns, one on each side of the radial zone.

- Refer back to the description of sea urchins in Section 1.4. (a) Where in living sea urchins is the mouth located? (b) Is this sea urchin likely to have been a burrower?

- (a) The mouth is located on the underside. (b) Most burrowers are oval or heart-shaped (Section 1.4); this specimen is round so it is unlikely to be a burrower (the huge spines would make borrowing difficult anyway).

This specimen is, in effect, upside down, and tilted at an angle to the flat base of the replica. In life position, the bottom of the sea urchin is relatively flat compared with the top, which cannot be seen in the replica. The jaw apparatus, which was used to rasp, pluck or scoop up its food, has fallen out (unlike in the Jurassic specimen shown in Figure 1.13).

Now use your hand lens to examine in detail one of the large knobs that once carried a spine. Such knobs, whatever their size, are called **tubercles**. If spines are absent, the size of the tubercles gives an approximate indication of their size. In the centre of each tubercle is a ball joint that fitted into a shallow socket at the base of the spine.

The sockets are clearly visible on the base of some detached spines. Muscles operating the spine were attached to the smooth area flanking the central ball joint. Look again at this smooth area with the lens. By comparing the detailed features of these spine-bearing plates with those of *modern* sea urchins, much can be deduced about how the spines were held and moved in fossil species.

- How do the larger tubercles and spines vary in size? Are they bigger nearer the centrally located mouth, or further away from it, towards where the test has its maximum girth?

- They get larger towards the test's maximum girth.

Now complete the drawing of the specimen started in Figure 4.20a in a similar level of detail. Add the following labels: *underside of sea urchin*; *ball joint for base of spine*; *large, club-shaped spine; position of mouth; radial zone of plates bearing tube feet*. Draw in a scale bar to represent 1 cm. Write in the genus and species name, *Tylocidaris clavigera*, and underline it.

(a)

(b)

Figure 4.20 (a) Fossil D in plan view (perpendicular to the flat base of the replica), with a missing area to be drawn in. (b) Space for drawing of a large tubercle and its vicinity.

Use the space in Figure 4.20b to draw a large tubercle and the area immediately around it. The latter is made up of much smaller tubercles, each of which has a tiny central ball joint that bore a minute spine (no longer present). Make sure you can see some of these very small tubercles with the hand lens. Do your drawing from an oblique angle, say about 45° to the surface, which will give a better idea of the large tubercle's shape than would a plan view. Label the following: *ball joint for base of spine*; *area for muscle attachment*; *very small tubercle with central ball joint*. Draw in a scale bar to represent 1 mm.

The spines, like the rest of the test, were made of the mineral calcite. In sea urchins this calcite is highly porous on a microscopic scale, with the pores occupied by soft tissue. Now think for a moment about the function of the spines. The lower spines could have been moved slowly and used in locomotion, but spines projected outwards in all directions, including upwards. This and their massive nature and club shape suggests another major function.

- What might that function have been?

- Defence against predators.

Such large and heavy spines were not easily broken, and would have made the sea urchin unpalatable to predators such as fish, crustaceans and octopuses, and also awkward to handle. You may have thought of other possible functions which seem equally plausible. For example, you may have wondered whether they were for sexual display, for use in combat between rivals competing for mates, or imagined they were for some other plausible purpose. How could you go about testing such ideas? Well fortunately, in this case, we have living relatives with which to make comparisons. This particular sea urchin, and the one shown in Figure 1.13, belong to a major group called the cidarids, that still thrive today, though both these species are extinct. Experts have concluded from studying living forms that the primary function of the spines in *Tylocidaris* was defence. They do not seem to have been for spreading the weight of the animal, nor for feeding (though in some other types of sea urchin, small spines help move food towards the mouth). Related species living today in rough water on rocky shorelines use their spines for anchorage in rock crevices, as well as for defence and locomotion, but there were few if any upstanding rocks on the Chalk sea floor (though there were hard surfaces in places).

In most fossil sea urchins the spines are often missing, having fallen off as the connecting tissues decayed within a few days of the death of the animal. Although isolated spines of this species can be found within the Chalk, the spines are often found attached.

- Was it likely that this sea urchin was exposed after death to persistent, strong currents? Give your reasoning.

- No. Strong currents would have broken off and dispersed the spines, not left them in place.

The sea urchin was probably covered over by a thick, protective layer of sediment (a preservational situation similar to that of the crinoid discussed in Question 3.2e). In this species, preservation of *in situ* spines was probably enhanced because the tissues connecting the heavy spines to the tubercles were tougher than usual and probably took longer to rot, increasing the chance of the intact sea urchin becoming covered in sediment.

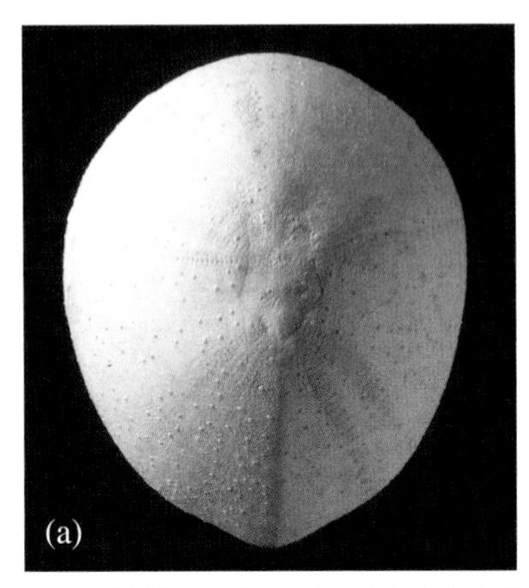

Figure 4.21 Irregular sea urchins from the Chalk viewed from above. In each case the mouth lies on the underside, towards the top of the picture of the specimen. (a) *Echinocorys scutata* (5 cm); (b) and (c) the genus *Micraster*. The specimen of *Micraster coranguinum* in (b) (5.5 cm) still retains its calcite plates, whereas that of *Micraster cortestudinarium* in (c) (6 cm) has lost its calcite plates and is preserved as a flint internal mould.

By analogy with its modern relatives, this cidarid species was a generalist in its eating habits, foraging off a variety of things on the sea floor, such as sponges, bryozoans (Box 3.1) or algal debris that had sunk down from higher up (the sea bed where it lived was too deep for algae to flourish).

The sexes are separate in sea urchins, but they are usually indistinguishable from the test alone. In the upper part of the test (not of course visible in this replica) there were calcite plates with a hole through which eggs or sperm were released into the water. One of these plates also had tiny perforations through which seawater could enter the internal hydraulic system linking up the tube feet to other water-filled structures inside. The animal expelled wastes through a centrally placed membrane at the top of the test.

Finally, to check your completed drawing of Figure 4.20b see Figure 4.30 at the end of this book; you can judge for yourself how good your labelled drawing in Figure 4.20a is!

Round forms like *Tylocidaris* are known as **regular sea urchins**. Figure 4.21 shows two other sea urchins, both common fossils in the Chalk. These are known as **irregular sea urchins** as they are less circular and more oval, like *Echinocorys* (Figure 4.21a), or heart shaped, like *Micraster* (Figure 4.21b,c). In irregular sea urchins, distinct front and back parts are developed because the animal moves forward with the test in a consistent orientation. As a result, the mouth tends not to be so centrally placed and it also lacks the robust jaw apparatus of the kind seen in Figure 1.13. Also, irregular echinoids expel waste to one side (the rear), not centrally at the top. *Echinocorys* lived on the sea floor, i.e. was epifaunal (Section 3.1.2). *Micraster* was infaunal, living in shallow burrows.

- The spines have fallen off the sea urchins in Figure 4.21. How do you think the size of their spines compares with those of *Tylocidaris*?

- Given the maximum size of their tubercles (especially tiny in *Echinocorys*), the spines must have been very much smaller than the largest ones of *Tylocidaris*.

Internal moulds of sea urchins preserved in flint are quite common, for example, in gravels and on shingle beaches of southern and eastern England. In such specimens (Figure 4.21c), the relatively soft calcite plates of the test have been worn away, leaving the hard flint infilling (see below for the origin of flint).

Other echinoderm fossils that occur in the Chalk include crinoids and starfish; these are more often found as isolated plates than whole specimens.

4.10.1 Some other life in the Chalk sea

The following is a selection of the many other fossil groups known from the Chalk.

Sponges

Sponges (Figure 4.22) are very common Chalk fossils, especially in the upper part of the Chalk, where they are often associated with **flint**. Flint occurs as hard nodules (lumps) in the upper Chalk. It formed by chemical reactions within the Chalk sediment soon after the sediment was laid down, and is composed of silica (SiO_2) in the form of microscopic quartz crystals. The silica was derived mainly from the skeletons of sponges made of silica (and from some smaller organisms with silica skeletons) that accumulated in the coccolith sediment forming the late Cretaceous sea floor. Being made of silica, the skeletons of dead sponges and other siliceous organisms tended to dissolve with time in the alkaline environment of the calcium carbonate sediment around them. The dissolved silica then resolidified on encountering localized acidic conditions. These acidic conditions arose when hydrogen sulphide gas (H_2S, 'rotten egg gas') coming off decaying organic matter met oxygen in aerated water coming down through burrows and other permeable parts of the sediment. Flints often have such strange shapes because the silica tended to resolidify in the vicinity of these animal burrows, replacing the calcium carbonate (calcite) sediment there which went into solution. Such flints are therefore trace fossils, albeit preserving rather approximate shapes of the original burrows. Being composed of hard silica, the highly resistant flint lumps tend to persist long after weathering and erosion of the softer Chalk.

Approximately spherical pieces of flint commonly have fossil sponges at their core, although often the original sponge has dissolved away, leaving a hollow, as in the top left specimen in Figure 4.22. Sponges occur in many other shapes, which may appear rather irregular, especially when partly or wholly surrounded by flint. They can often be identified because of their porous, spongy texture within.

Cephalopods

Ammonites are common at some levels in the Chalk (especially the lower part), but the aragonite shell tends to be dissolved away, leaving only moulds. Figure 4.23 shows two forms. *Turrilites* looks at first like a gastropod, but is in fact an ammonite in which the chambered shell is coiled in the form of a helix (see also Section 4.6). Belemnites (Figure 4.23c) also occur sporadically.

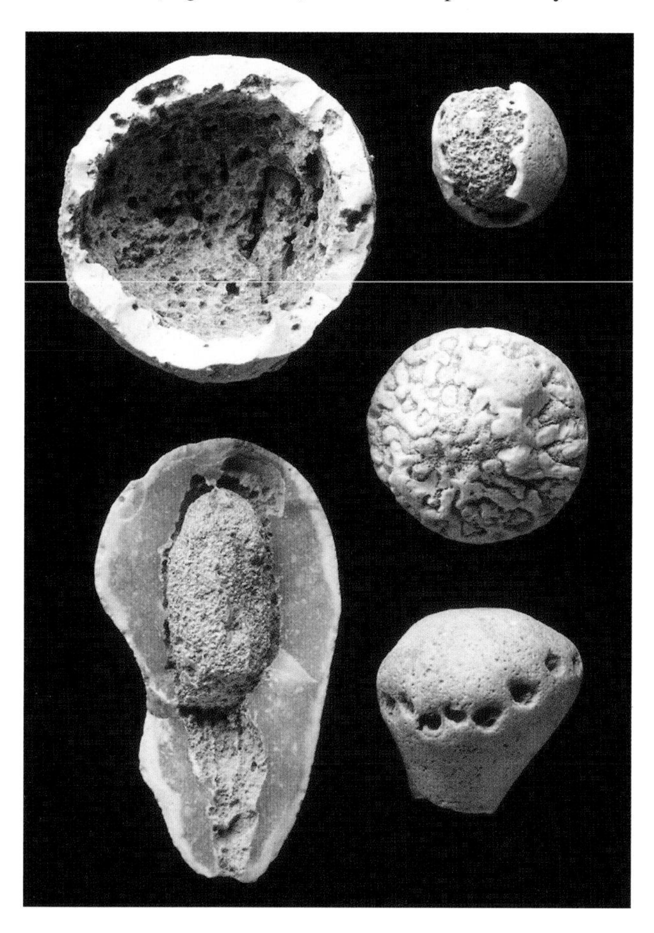

Figure 4.22 A variety of sponges from the Chalk, preserved in association with flint. The largest round specimen is nearly 4 cm in diameter.

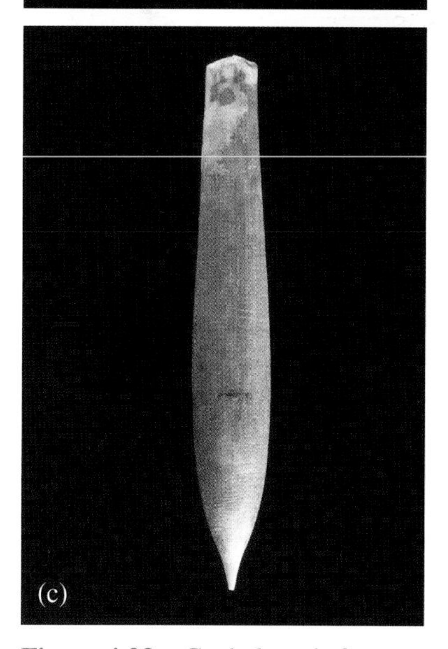

Figure 4.23 Cephalopods from the Chalk. (a) The ammonite *Schloenbachia varians* (6.5 cm); (b) the ammonite *Turrilites costatus* (8 cm); (c) the belemnite *Actinocamax plenus* (7 cm).

Bivalves

Among the many bivalves that occur in the Chalk are *Inoceramus* (Figure 4.24a), which may exceed 30 cm in length; *Spondylus* (Figure 4.24b), which has strong ridges (ribs), some bearing spines; and *Pycnodonte* (Figure 4.24c), which like other oysters is very variable in shape. These are all calcitic forms; bivalves with aragonitic shells lived there too, but are less often preserved, as are the aragonitic shells of ammonites and some gastropods.

(a)

(b)

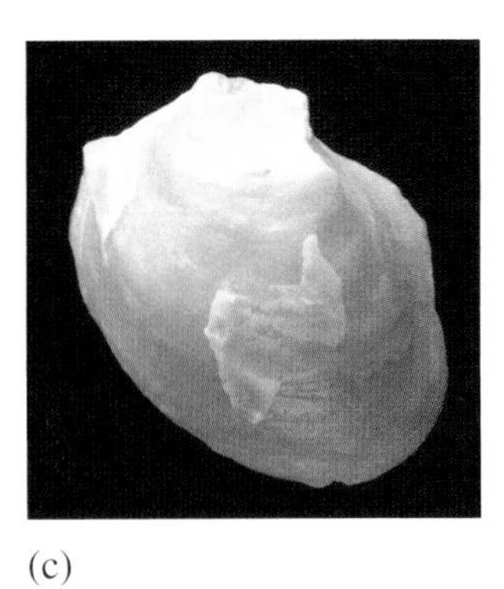

(c)

Figure 4.24 Bivalves from the Chalk. (a) *Inoceramus lamarcki* (9 cm); (b) *Spondylus spinosus* (5.5 cm); (c) *Pycnodonte vesiculare* (2.5 cm).

Brachiopods

Figure 4.25 shows just two of the many species of brachiopods that can be found in the Chalk. Like echinoderms, which also have calcite shells, they tend to be well preserved.

(a)

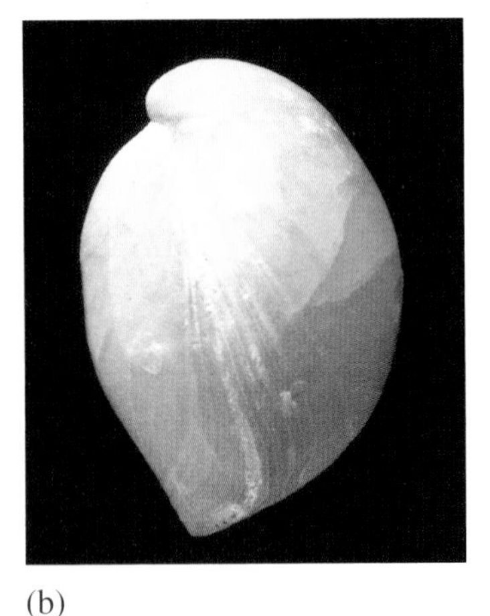

(b)

Figure 4.25 Brachiopods from the Chalk. (a) *Orbirhynchia cuvieri* (2 cm); (b) *Gibbithyris semiglobosa* (2 cm).

Vertebrates

Fish scales occur sporadically, and usually show up clearly against the white Chalk as shiny brown or pink flakes, 1–2 mm long. Shark teeth are quite common. The teeth of the shark *Ptychodus* (Figure 4.26a) were adapted for crushing shells of invertebrates, such as ammonites and bivalves, whilst many other shark genera had teeth of a more typical shape, as in *Cretolamna* (Figure 4.26b). Reptile remains are rare and fragmentary, but include all the main late Cretaceous marine groups, including turtles, ichthyosaurs, plesiosaurs, and mosasaurs. Even rarer are pterosaur teeth and bones. There is just a single record of a dinosaur in the British Chalk — fragments of an ankylosaur; presumably its carcass got washed out to sea and floated awhile before sinking.

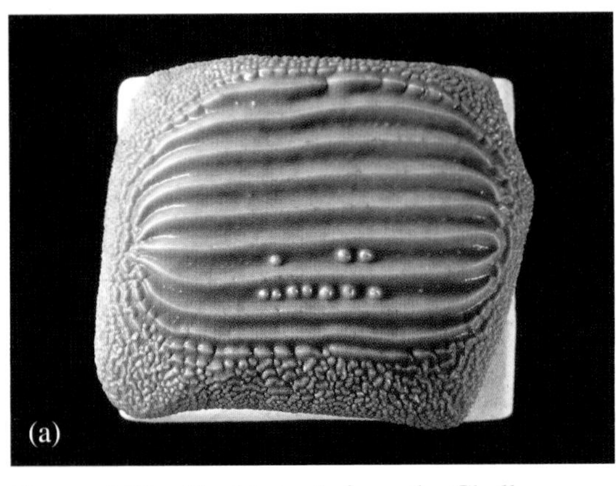

Figure 4.26 Shark's teeth from the Chalk. (a) *Ptychodus polygyrus* (4.5 cm); (b) *Cretolamna woodwardi* (2.5 cm).

4.11 End of an era — the Cretaceous–Tertiary (K–T) mass extinction

In the mid nineteenth century, palaeontologists recognized that the end of the Cretaceous Period marked such a major event in the history of life that it should be designated the end of an era.

- Which era ended and which era began?
- The Mesozoic Era ended and the Cenozoic Era began.

Now read the *Atlas*, pp.122–123, 126–127 and 128–129 (leaving pp.124–125 for a moment). Note that the percentages in the text on the top right of p.129 of the *Atlas*, e.g. 'lizards (6%)', refer to the proportion of families in each group that became extinct. Remember that Box 3.1 also mentions some of the major casualties of the end-Cretaceous mass extinction.

- Why is the boundary between the Mesozoic and Cenozoic eras also known as the K–T boundary?
- 'K' is short for *kreide*, German for chalk. (K is, in fact, the international symbol geologists use for the Cretaceous.) 'T' is short for Tertiary (*Atlas*, p.122 and *Atlas G*, p.210).

In 1980, a now famous paper was published that rekindled the long-running debate about the causes of mass extinctions. Walter Alvarez, an American geologist, analysed the thin clay layer that precisely marks the K–T boundary at Gubbio in Italy (Figure 4.27a) and revealed it had an abnormally high concentration of the metallic element iridium. In an attempt to understand events at the K–T boundary, he had enlisted the expertise of his father, Luis Alvarez, a Nobel-prizewinning particle physicist. As iridium is very rare in the Earth's crust but relatively abundant in certain meteorites, they interpreted its high concentration in the clay layer as fallout from the impact of a very large meteorite 65 million years ago. Together, they proposed that this meteorite was responsible for wiping out the dinosaurs and much else besides. This hypothesis (working idea) immediately triggered a massive research programme.

Figure 4.27 (a) The clay layer at the K–T boundary at Gubbio in Italy, where the anomalously high concentration of iridium at this level was first discovered. A rich variety of fossil plankton occurs below the boundary, but few forms survived into the layer above it. A pencil for scale rests on the thin dark clay layer in these tilted beds. (b) Minute spheres (0.5–1 mm in diameter) in the K–T boundary clay that have cooled rapidly from droplets of molten rock.

(a)

(b)

- How big is the meteorite estimated to have been, and about how fast was it travelling when it struck?

- About 10 km in diameter, travelling at about 30 km per second (*Atlas*, p.126).

Since 1980, the evidence for an end-Cretaceous impact event has become overwhelming. Iridium anomalies have been found at over 100 K–T sites around the world. In the thin boundary layer are splash-shaped glassy droplets and tiny spheres resulting from rapid cooling of melted rock ejected into the atmosphere (Figure 4.27b). Grains of quartz, normally clear under the microscope, show parallel lines produced by the shock of intense pressure ('shocked quartz', *Atlas*, p.123 and *Atlas G*, p.214). In places the boundary layer even contains microdiamonds (*Atlas*, p.126 and *Atlas G*, p.211): the intense pressures and high temperatures caused some calcium carbonate in limestone at the impact site to be converted in part to diamond, a form of carbon.

- What is the K–T impact crater called, where is it located, and why is it so inconspicuous?

- The Chicxulub Crater, which is centred on the coast of northern Yucatan, Mexico. There is no visible crater now as it is filled with a deep layer of sediments, having been mostly under water since the impact (*Atlas*, pp.126–127).

The huge impact that caused the Chicxulub Crater would have generated enormous earthquakes and there is some evidence that it produced giant waves (tsunamis) (*Atlas*, p.123 and *Atlas G*, p.215). As we have just seen, the impact ejected a wide variety of materials, including dust and tiny droplets of molten rock, into the atmosphere, and these may well have darkened the skies for months.

- What effect would this darkening have had on plants, large and small, and why are detrimental effects on plants also detrimental to animal life?

- The darkening would have prevented plants in the oceans and on land from photosynthesizing normally. Plants are the basis of the food chain (*Atlas G*, p.208), and their loss also affects the herbivores which eat them, and the carnivores that eat the herbivores (*Atlas*, p.128).

Phytoplankton (Section 3.1.2) suffered intense casualties at the K–T boundary, especially the minute phytoplankton whose calcite plates (coccoliths) accumulated on the late Cretaceous sea bed to form Chalk deposits (Section 4.10). Figure 4.28a shows a coccolith of a species that did not survive the K–T boundary. As phytoplankton are at the base of the oceanic food chain, their loss would potentially have affected a very large number of ocean species. Without photosynthesis (during which plants absorb carbon dioxide), carbon dioxide would have built up in the atmosphere, causing global warming. Many species of zooplankton (Section 3.1.2), such as planktonic forams (Figure 4.28b), were also reduced by at least 90%. The boundary layer (Figure 4.27a) probably represents a time period of between about 10 000 to 100 000 years; unfortunately, geologists cannot resolve time intervals of less than 100 000 years in rocks as old as 65 million years, so it is not possible to be sure how long the plankton extinctions took.

Question 4.7 Test your understanding of some effects of the impact, and the fortunes of plant life at the end of the Cretaceous, by filling in the blank spaces in the following summary paragraphs with the appropriate words or numbers.

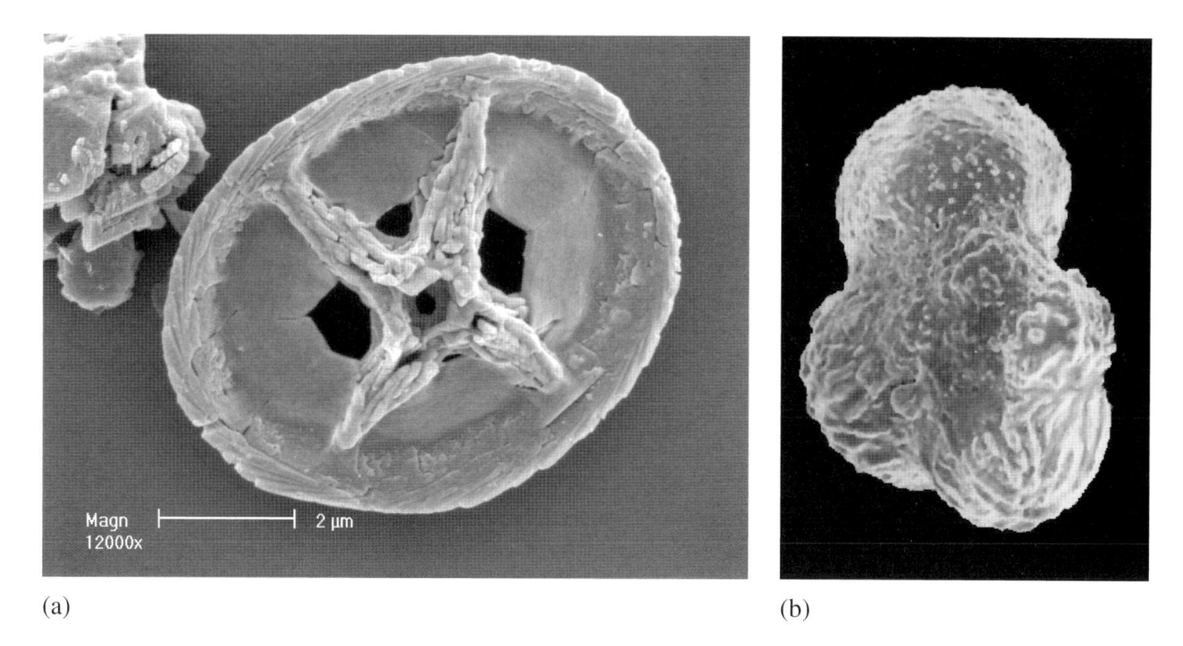

(a) (b)

Figure 4.28 Two microfossil species found in Chalk that became extinct at the K–T boundary. (a) A coccolith plate from *Eiffelithus turriseiffelii* with other coccolith debris (top left). Note the scale bar: the plate is only 0.008 mm across. (b) The planktonic foram *Rugoglobigerina macrocephala* (0.25 mm).

Soot in the form of .... (1) particles found in strata at the K–T boundary is thought to be evidence for .... (2) that initially swept across the Americas, and then extended globally, sparked off by electric storms setting alight to dead and dying vegetation. The global effect of the impact, both short and long term, has been likened to that of a 'nuclear winter' scenario. Rock dust ejected from the impact, droplets of molten rock, and smoke and soot from the wildfires would have darkened skies causing atmospheric temperatures to .... (3) at first. But then .... (4) may soon have been promoted by a build-up of CO_2 in the atmosphere, caused by the suppression of photosynthesis and by the release of CO_2 into the atmosphere by the chemical breakdown of limestone rock (calcium carbonate) vaporized by the impact. Large quantities of water vapour ejected into the atmosphere would itself also have caused a greenhouse effect and promoted global warming. Sulphur (in the form of sulphur oxides) was probably released into the atmosphere from the heating of rocks rich in gypsum (calcium sulphate) in the impact area. The sulphur oxides then dissolved in rainwater to fall as .... (5), affecting ponds, lakes and rivers, killing some aquatic life and further damaging plant life in general.

Plants in the .... (6) hemisphere were barely affected by the end-Cretaceous extinctions, although evidence from Hell Creek suggests that .... % (7) of plant species became locally extinct in the interior of North .... (8). Among the worst hit were the newly evolved .... (9), along with some of the common Mesozoic plants such as ginkgos and cycads. The first plants to recover from the immediate effects of the impact seem to have been .... (10), which today are often the first plants to return to landscapes devastated by volcanic eruptions. ◀

- Apart from the huge meteorite impact, what other major geological event at this time may have contributed to the extinctions?

- Large-scale volcanic eruptions in the Deccan region of India (the Deccan Traps) emitted huge quantities of fumes and gases that could have caused various problems for life, including climate change. In particular, the carbon dioxide may have boosted global warming (*Atlas*, p.123).

The word 'Traps' in Deccan Traps is derived from the Swedish for 'staircase', referring to the stepped topography that a thick series of lavas such as this often shows when dissected by weathering. Note that the timing of the Deccan and other flood basalts since the early Permian is shown on p.91 of the *Atlas*, as are known asteroid or comet impacts since the Cambrian, with an indication of size.

Now read the *Atlas*, pp.124–125.

Question 4.8 Check the following statements concerning reptiles at the end of the Cretaceous Period, and correct any errors, if present.

(a) In general, there is no evidence that dinosaurs were in decline before the K–T impact. Among saurischian dinosaurs, the tyrannosaurids, for example, were flourishing up until the end of the Cretaceous, and other predatory theropod groups, such as the ostrich-like ornithomimids, also showed no decline during the last few million years before the meteorite struck.

(b) Ornithischian dinosaurs that survived to late Cretaceous times in North America included the horned *Triceratops*, the duck-billed hadrosaur *Edmontosaurus* and the head-butting pachycephalosaurid *Stegosaurus*.

(c) *Quetzalcoatlus* was a flying dinosaur with a wingspan of 12 metres. ◀

In summary, although a massive impact certainly occurred at the end of the Cretaceous Period, and appears to have led particularly to the mass extinction of plankton, it seems to have had little or nothing to do with some, perhaps most, of the other extinctions occurring around this time (Box 3.1). A massive reduction in phytoplankton, in addition to a wide range of physical and chemical effects resulting from the impact, could have led to a cascade of extinctions. But some groups had already become extinct over a million years before the impact, and for others the impact seems to have been the final blow, coming at a bad time. Yet other groups were unscathed. The relatively short-lived global events at the K–T boundary occurred within a context of much longer term environmental change, including the lowering of sea level and global cooling, and a sustained period of biological change. The diversity of ammonites, for example, had been slowly declining for some millions of years, though recent research shows that what was left of the group became abruptly extinct at the K–T boundary. The details of dinosaur extinction are still much debated. Unfortunately, the precise extinction pattern of many animal groups, though increasingly well understood, remains somewhat ambiguous, due mainly to the limitations of the fossil record. As stated in Section 3.10.1, the complexity of the Earth's natural systems makes it difficult if not impossible to establish the full chain of cause and effect during extinctions.

4.12 Summary of Mesozoic life

The Mesozoic Era began with many forms of life struggling to recover from the devastating extinction at the end of the Permian. Such strugglers were relatively lucky; some groups had gone forever. Fossils, both marine and non-marine, are generally uncommon in the early Triassic. There were no early Triassic corals, for example. The scleractinian corals only appeared in the middle Triassic, and they flourish to this day.

The early Mesozoic saw very important changes in land-dwelling vertebrates. In the Triassic, the cynodonts replaced the older synapsids of the Permian. They developed increasingly mammal-like features, such as being warm-blooded and having hair. The first mammals appeared in the late Triassic, and for much of the Mesozoic mammals remained small, shrew-like animals living in the nooks and crannies of the dinosaur world. The structure of the ear is used, somewhat arbitrarily, to distinguish the early mammals from mammal-like reptiles: reptiles have one bone in the middle ear, mammals have three.

Supporting all Mesozoic animal life on land was a distinctive plant-based food chain, dominated by conifers, cycads and to a lesser extent ferns. The pteridosperms, which had survived the Permian extinction, persisted until the mid Cretaceous, and the bennettitales were a group that evolved, flourished and died out within the Mesozoic. In the early Cretaceous one group of plants gradually acquired the suite of characters that define flowering plants today — the angiosperms; these became important by the late Cretaceous.

Dinosaurs first appeared in the late Triassic, and reached their greatest diversity in the late Cretaceous. There were two groups, distinguished mainly by their pelvic structure. The saurischians included bipedal carnivores and quadrupedal herbivores. The ornithischians were all herbivores, and were either bipedal or quadrupedal. Birds arose in the late Jurassic from a group of small bipedal saurischian dinosaurs. Recent finds of feathered, non-flying dinosaurs reveal that feathers have not always been a character unique to birds.

The Mesozoic Era is often characterized as the 'Age of Reptiles'. Dinosaurs are only part of this Mesozoic success story, however, for they never took to the air (except those that evolved into birds) or to the oceans. The flying Mesozoic reptiles were the pterosaurs, which ate mainly fish. Marine reptile groups which appeared, flourished and died out all within the Mesozoic included the nothosaurs, placodonts, ichthyosaurs, plesiosaurs, pliosaurs and mosasaurs. These were the top predators in the sea, along with crocodiles (also reptiles) and sharks.

The seas of the Jurassic and Cretaceous abounded with life, including ammonites, which were cephalopod molluscs with spiral, chambered shells. They evolved many different species in the Jurassic and Cretaceous, and some groups even became partially uncoiled, or coiled into unusual shapes. Other cephalopods swimming in the sea alongside ammonites were the squid-like belemnites, whose solid, bullet-shaped internal skeletons are common fossils. Among the many bivalves in the Jurassic sea were thick-shelled oysters, a group whose shells lack the more usual bivalve symmetry.

In the late Cretaceous, countless billions of tiny coccolith plates from phytoplankton carpeted the sea floor, and they form the bulk of the sedimentary rock called Chalk. Among the commonly found fossils in the Chalk are groups that lived on (or, in some cases, just below) the sea floor, such as sea urchins, sponges, bivalves and brachiopods, along with some nektonic ammonites and belemnites that sank to the sea bed. Shells or skeletons made of calcite are better preserved than those made of aragonite, which tended to dissolve.

A massive meteorite impact certainly occurred at the end of the Cretaceous Period, 65 Ma ago, off what is now the Mexican coast. The many environmental disturbances, which included a darkening of the skies, appear to have led particularly to the mass extinction of plankton. But the relatively short-lived global events at the K–T boundary occurred within a context of much longer term environmental change, and the impact seems to have had little or nothing to do with some, perhaps most, of the other extinctions occurring around this time. Some groups, like ichthyosaurs, had already become extinct long before the impact. For others the impact appears to have been the final blow. Ammonites, for example, had been slowly declining for millions of years, though what was left of the group became abruptly extinct at the K–T boundary. The same seems also to be true of dinosaurs, but their fossil record is too poor to be sure of their precise extinction pattern.

The extinctions at the end of the Mesozoic re-set the evolutionary stage, providing opportunities for groups that had been more or less waiting in the wings during the Mesozoic Era, such as the flowering plants, insects, birds and mammals. Let's now look at the fortunes of these and other groups in the next and current Era — the Cenozoic.

Life in the Cenozoic

First, let's put the duration of the Cenozoic Era into perspective. Look again at Figure 1.14.

- Have any geological *periods* during the Phanerozoic been as long as the Cenozoic *Era*? If so, which periods are they?

- Yes, the Cretaceous Period (77 Ma). The Devonian, Carboniferous and Jurassic are each within 1 or 2 Ma of being as long as the Cenozoic Era (65 Ma).

- Which geological period has by far the shortest duration of the entire Phanerozoic?

- The Quaternary Period (1.8 Ma).

As we saw in Section 1.5, geologists have divided the history of the Earth into time intervals of *varying* duration because the boundaries between eras and periods are based on events like mass extinctions, climate changes and mountain building which don't happen in a regular, clock-like fashion. In the case of the Quaternary Period, the climate became so different about 2 Ma ago (as we will see in Section 5.6), and the resulting deposits are so widespread and distinctive, that geologists consider that this brief interval merits a period of its own.

5.1 The Early Tertiary

Read the *Atlas*, pp.130–131.

Note that the *Atlas* talks of the 'Tertiary Period', though strictly speaking the Tertiary is a sub-Era containing two periods — the **Palaeogene** and **Neogene**, as you can see from Figure 1.14. The epochs making up these periods (e.g. the Eocene) are shown in the geological timescale on p.164 of the *Atlas*.

Let's consider briefly the global setting in which Cenozoic life was evolving. The break-up of the southern continents of Gondwana that had begun in the early Mesozoic continued during the Cenozoic, eventually producing the basic plate configuration of the modern world. The continents of Africa and India moved north and collided with the southern flank of Eurasia (Europe and Asia), throwing up the great east–west belt of mountains that runs from the Alps to the Himalayas. Such 'collisions' take place almost imperceptibly slowly — nothing like a collision between motor cars. A popular analogy for the average rate at which plates move around the Earth is the rate at which fingernails grow — just two or three cm per year. If you wish, you can read more about the formation of the Himalayas and the Tibetan Plateau on pp.142–143 of the *Atlas*.

The rifting apart of the North Atlantic began about 60 Ma ago over a 'hot spot' (*Atlas G*, p.209) where Iceland is today. For about 10 Ma, there was intense volcanic activity in what is now the northwest British Isles as this area started rifting away from Greenland (see the globe on p.130 of the *Atlas*). The volcanism ceased in both areas as they moved laterally away from the hot spot (and from each other). The legacy of this volcanism is the rugged scenery of many islands of northwest Scotland, such the Isle of Skye (an early Tertiary volcano) and, in Northern Ireland, the Giant's

Causeway (an early Tertiary lava flow). The volcanic activity continues to this day in the middle of the Atlantic where new ocean crust is being generated (*Atlas*, p.175). If you wish, you can read more about the opening of the North Atlantic and the associated volcanic activity on pp.134–135 of the *Atlas*.

Life began recovering from the end Cretaceous mass extinction in earliest Tertiary times. For example, only a few groups of birds managed to survive the K–T extinction, but these soon diversified into many of the major groups found today. As the Tertiary proceeded, plant groups that had dominated the Jurassic and most of the Cretaceous, especially the cycads and conifers, continued their decline (Figure 3.15), while the flowering plants (angiosperms) literally bloomed. As we saw in Section 4.9, the expansion of the angiosperms had already begun back in the mid Cretaceous. Their typically deciduous habit of seasonally shedding leaves (unlike the predominantly evergreen cycads and conifers) seems to have given them an advantage during and after the end Cretaceous extinction event. In early Tertiary times angiosperms quickly become the dominant vegetation, ranging in size from small weeds and shrubs to large trees with strong woody stems. The runaway success of the angiosperms was in part due to their specialized adaptations produced by coevolution (Section 3.7) with insects, birds and, in the Cenozoic, with new types of mammals.

5.2 The radiation of the mammals

Extinction is, as we have seen, forever. But, depending on one's perspective, mass extinctions aren't always bad news. For example, the mass extinction of dinosaurs and other large reptiles at the end of the Cretaceous Period seems to have cleared the way for mammals to expand into vacated niches, and 65 Ma later it's even keeping some of their descendants employed trying to find out how it all happened.

Look at Figure 5.1, which shows the distribution in time of the major groups (mainly Orders) of mammals from the start of the Jurassic Period, and their evolutionary relationships. The width of each group on the diagram gives a rough indication of its diversity.

- What rather arbitrary criterion is used to distinguish the earliest mammals from mammal-like reptiles?

- Mammals have three bones in the middle ear: reptiles have only one. The two bones that form the jaw joint in reptiles became incorporated into the middle ear of mammals (Section 4.4).

We met some of the early mammals in Section 4.4 and when reading p.117 of the *Atlas* in Section 4.8.2. Figure 5.1 shows some of the various extinct mammal groups that appeared in the Mesozoic, e.g. the morganucodonts (*Atlas*, p.107), triconodonts and multituberculates (*Atlas*, p.117). The **multituberculates** were the most abundant of the extinct mammal groups, and were probably nocturnal, plant-eating, gerbil-like animals adapted for running and burrowing (*Atlas*, p.117). Judging by the size of their teeth and other rare skeletal remains, most other Mesozoic mammals were also small, shrew-like creatures. They may well have been generally nocturnal, living in nooks and crannies amongst rocks and plant roots, and possibly burrowing.

Many of the extinct early mammal groups are known only from isolated teeth and fragments of jawbones, and their evolutionary relationships are obscure. Mammal teeth, in contrast to the simple, peg-shaped teeth of reptiles, are differentiated into

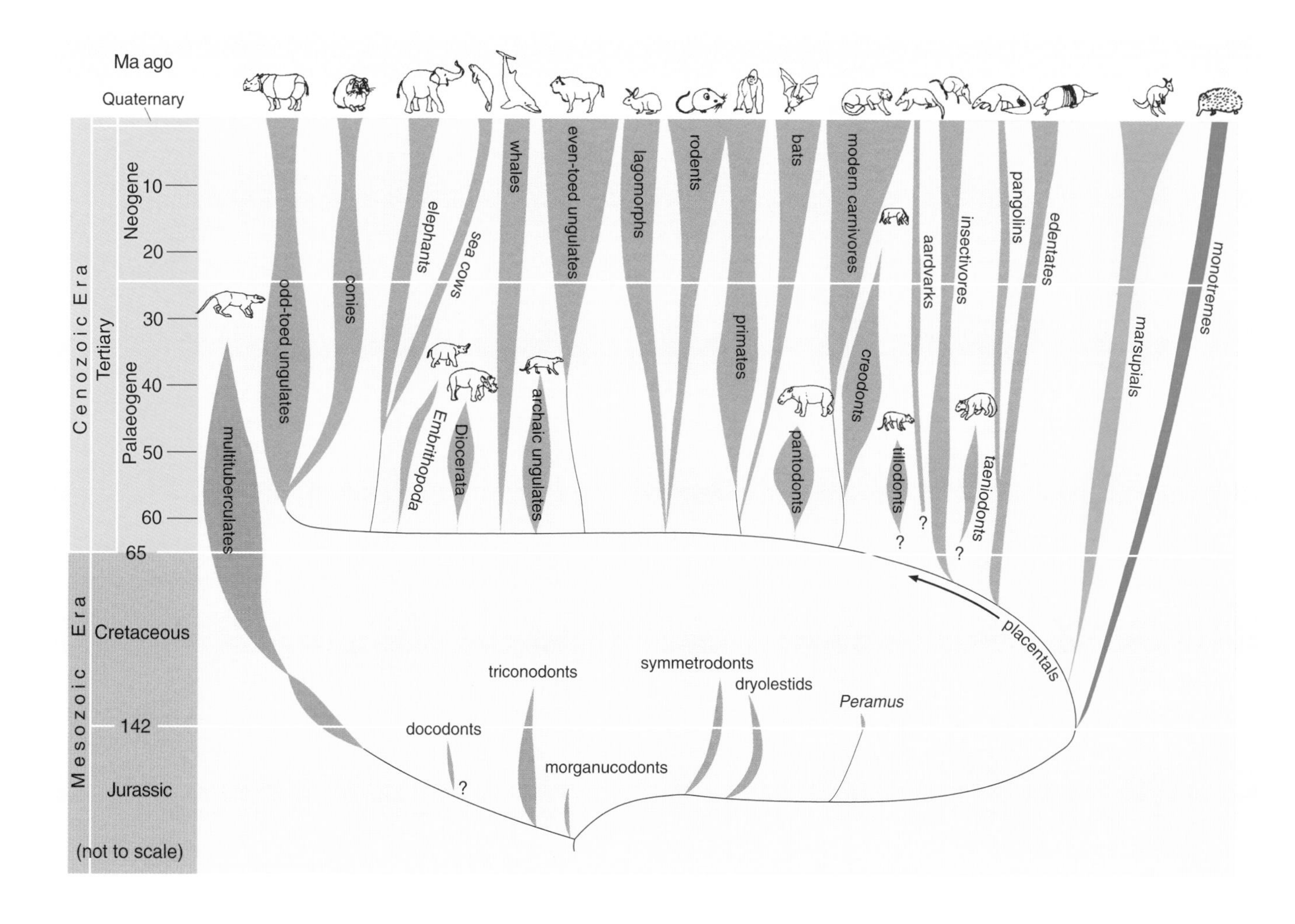

teeth of different function. Incisors and canines at the front of the mouth are used for obtaining food (e.g. biting off fruit or attacking prey) and holding it, and cheek teeth at the side of the mouth prepare the food for digestion (Section 3.9.1). The cheek teeth (molars and premolars) have distinctive patterns of cusps, ridges and furrows which, in combination with movement of the jaws in quite complicated ways, allows for cutting and chewing. The detailed form of fossil mammal teeth and their pattern of wear often give an indication of diet, and a surprising amount of information can thus be gained even from a single tooth (as in the case of *Purgatorius* mentioned on p.107 of the *Atlas*).

Figure 5.1 The pattern of evolutionary radiation in mammals. See text for explanation.

Today there are three main groups of mammals, all of which had their origin in the Cretaceous. The **placental** mammals are much more dominant than the other two groups — the **monotremes** and **marsupials**. The monotremes, normally regarded as the most primitive of today's three groups, have retained the reptilian habit of laying eggs; they include the duck-billed platypus and the spiny anteater. The marsupials, such as kangaroos, give birth to live young but at such a premature stage of development that they have to be carried around for a while by the mother in a special pouch. It is no accident that the living monotremes and marsupials have survived in that remnant of Gondwana, Australasia (Australia, New Zealand, Tasmania, etc.), which has been cut off from more modern mammals by its isolation as a continent since the late Cretaceous. Likewise, a great many types of marsupials once inhabited another large fragment of Gondwana, South America, though their diversity declined after it was reconnected with North America in late Tertiary times (Section 5.2.1).

According to Figure 5.1, has the diversity of the monotremes changed much since their origin in the early Cretaceous, and how does their diversity compare with that of the placentals?

As shown in the diagram, the width of the bar for monotremes remains thin from its origin to the present, whereas the bars for many separate orders of placentals are wider than that of the monotremes. The diversity of monotremes has therefore changed little since their origin, and has remained much less than that of the placentals.

Like other Mesozoic mammals, the early placentals were small shrew-like animals, such as *Zalambdalestes* from the Cretaceous of Mongolia (*Atlas*, p.107 and pp.116–117). Placentals nourish their embryos within the uterus through the placenta, a special tissue connected to the mother, which supplies nutrients and removes the waste products of the embryo's metabolism. The placentals therefore often had a competitive advantage over more primitive mammals such as the monotremes, marsupials and multituberculates: they bore relatively well-developed live young.

The massive expansion of placental mammals in the early Cenozoic is an example of an **evolutionary radiation** — an episode of rapid and sustained increase in diversity, often involving the origin of many new groups above the species level such as orders and families. Over 15 major groups of placental mammals evolved within the first 10 Ma of the Cenozoic (Figure 5.1 and the *Atlas*, p.131), although six of these died out by about 40 Ma ago.

About how long had mammals been in existence before their spectacular radiation in the early Cenozoic around 60 Ma ago? You may need to refer back to Figure 3.14.

About 150 Ma. Mammals first appeared in the late Triassic, 210 Ma ago.

This early Tertiary burst of evolution produced mammals adapted to a huge range of modes of life and environments — think for a moment of today's flying bats, swimming dolphins, burrowing moles, running cheetahs, tree-climbing monkeys, and so on. And, ever since early Tertiary times, most of the world's largest animals have been mammals, as is true today — the elephant and the blue whale are Earth's largest land and sea animals. Only the blue whale, however, compares to the size of the sauropod dinosaurs.

Comparisons of the skeletons of living and extinct mammals have long been used to infer evolutionary relationships. This has led, for example, to the placing of monotremes as the most primitive of living mammal groups, and the grouping together of lagomorphs (rabbits, etc.) with rodents (rats, etc.), as in Figure 5.1. However, as we saw in Section 1.7, recent DNA analysis and sequencing has thrown up a number of surprises that appear to contradict some relationships based on skeletal morphology alone. Insectivores (such as the hedgehog) seem to be more primitive than monotremes, and lagomorphs appear to be more closely related to primates than to rodents (*Atlas*, p.195). It will be interesting to see if further work substantiates these relationships.

5.2.1 Mammals of the Americas

Read the *Atlas*, pp.148–149. Note that the horse *Merychippus* roamed the American prairies about 17 to 11 Ma ago, not 5–10 Ma ago as stated on p.149. Note also that a much greater span of time is discussed in these pages than implied by the globe placed at 5 Ma ago on the timeline.

The evolutionary effects of geographical isolation are well illustrated by the ancient mammals of the Americas. For much of the last 200 Ma, North and South America have been isolated from one another by a seaway. Consequently, their isolated mammalian faunas have tended to evolve along separate lines, but now and then a temporary land connection between the two continents has been established. Such land bridges have allowed two-way traffic, i.e. the exchange of animal species, which has sometimes led to extinctions.

Question 5.1 Correct any errors in the following statements.

(a) About 3 Ma ago, opossums and some xenarthrans (such as the plant-eating ground sloths) moved from North America into South America.

(b) Glyptodonts were South American marsupials that superficially resembled the group of dinosaurs called ankylosaurs.

(c) The probable ancestor of all horses, *Hyracotherium*, was about twice the size of a modern horse.

(d) The interchange of mammals across the Central American 'freeway' about 3 Ma ago resulted in far higher levels of extinction in South America than in North America, and the total mammal population in South America was drastically reduced. ◀

5.2.2 Messel

In 1995, the Messel Quarry near Frankfurt in Germany was declared a World Heritage Site because of the quality of its preservation of an Eocene ecosystem, especially its mammals, many of which even have gut contents and hair preserved. Some of the Messel birds still retain all their feathers. A wide diversity of animals and plants is found in these ancient lake sediments where the oxygen-poor bottom waters and fine-grained sediment favoured preservation (Section 1.2). The decomposition of organic matter was incomplete and the resulting 'oil shales' at Messel were once worked for the petroleum compounds they contain. Like the Cambrian Burgess Shale site in Canada (Section 3.1.1) and the Jurassic limestones of Solenhofen, also in Germany (Section 4.5.1), the Messel discoveries provide an exceptional window onto ancient life, revealing the extent to which mammals had evolved specialized forms (e.g. bats) quite early in their radiation.

Now read the *Atlas*, pp.132–133. Note that the spectacular fossil turtle shown on p.131 of the *Atlas* is also from Messel, as is the kangaroo rat pictured below it. Another specimen of the early horse *Propalaeotherium* is shown on p.193 of the *Atlas*.

The striking similarity between certain marsupial mammals of Australia and placental mammals of other continents today is one of the best known general cases of convergent evolution, a phenomenon we met earlier in Section 4.3. Evolution has a remarkable capacity to generate similar adaptations independently in different lineages in response to similar selection pressures. For example, at least five orders of mammals evolved convergently the specialized habit of eating ants; all show morphological features linked with that peculiar diet — long snouts, reduced or little-used teeth, and strong claws on forelimbs for digging into ant or termite nests. Today, the ant-eating members of these five orders are distributed over four continents: the spiny anteater, or spiny echidna (a monotreme) and the numbat (a marsupial) are both found in Australia; the aardvark (a placental) inhabits parts of tropical Africa; the pangolin (placental) is found in northern and western Africa, and in Southeast Asia; and the ant bear or anteater (placental) lives in the South American tropics. No pair of these five distinct living groups of mammalian anteaters is believed to have shared an ancestor possessing the specialized features associated with a diet of ants. The Messel deposits contain the oldest known anteaters, including one form (*Eurotamandia*) related to the living anteaters of South America and another form (*Eomanis*) very similar to modern pangolins. Reconstructions of both these genera are shown on pp.132–133 of the *Atlas*.

5.3 The mid Tertiary

Read the *Atlas*, pp.138–139. The end of the caption to the 'Amber frog' on p.138 should say '... at a time of *lower* sea levels than shown in the maps'.

As the *Atlas* states on p.139, the percentage of modern North America under the sea had dropped from 60% at the start of the Cenozoic, to only 5% by mid Tertiary times. A net withdrawal of the seas over the entire Cenozoic affected every continent (see the *Atlas*, p.91). This global fall in sea level is the main reason why Cenozoic marine fossils are relatively rare in inland areas of many countries, including Britain.

By mid Tertiary times, the continents were getting close to their present positions and the world's overall climate was changing.

- What happened to global climates about 25 Ma ago?

- The Earth's climates changed from being warm and humid to being cooler and drier as the Antarctic ice cap had begun to develop (*Atlas*, pp.138–139). (Cold air is drier simply because it can hold less humidity.) In retrospect, it can be seen that the Earth was gradually descending towards the Quaternary Ice Age.

The origin of the **grasses** (*Atlas G*, p.209) was one of the most important recent evolutionary developments in flowering plants, and it also had far-reaching effects on animal life. As explained in the box 'Shorter growing time' on p.139 of the *Atlas*, grasses were good at coping with the shorter growing seasons and more fluctuating conditions that developed in mid Tertiary times. Forests and woods diminished and were replaced on many continents by open **savanna** (*Atlas G*, p.214). This savanna grassland with rare, scattered trees is also called prairie, steppe, pampas or veldt. Today, there are nearly 10 000 species of grasses. In the early Miocene, another very important plant group called the Compositae originated. There are now about 25 000 species in this family, including plants such as daisies, thistles, sunflowers and lettuce, and also many weeds. As any gardener knows, weeds are particularly good at growing in disturbed environments such as a dug-over garden bed, and the newly evolved composite weeds similarly thrived in the more fluctuating, less predictable climates of the mid Tertiary.

The developing savannas of the mid Tertiary favoured **grazers** (mainly grass eaters, *Atlas G*, p.209). Hoofed mammals such as horses were originally small, forest-dwelling **browsers** (*Atlas G*, p.205) nibbling on soft leaves, twigs and shoots, e.g. the early horse *Hyracotherium* (*Atlas*, p.149). Now they took advantage of the spread of the grasses, a new food material. Grazing does little damage to grasses because they can regrow from the base and propagate by underground runners, giving them an advantage over many other plants. Think about mowing a lawn: cutting off the upper tips by this artificial form of grazing does little or no harm to the grass. Even so, like most plants, grasses have evolved various defences, of which the most important is the inclusion of tiny crystals of hard silica in the leaves. These jagged little crystals rapidly wore away the teeth of the early grazers. If a grazer's teeth wore down completely, it could no longer eat, so individuals with longer teeth and thicker enamel were favoured by natural selection. As was mentioned on p.149 of the *Atlas*, *Merychippus* (about 1 m high at the shoulder) was one of the first horses to feed almost entirely on grass; it had taller and higher-crowned teeth than those of its ancestors.

Compare the fossil skeleton of *Mesohippus* (*Atlas*, p.138), a genus which lived 37 to 32 Ma ago and was about 60 cm high at the shoulder, with that of the similar-sized *Propalaeotherium* (*Atlas*, p.133), which lived about 15 Ma earlier. The back of *Mesohippus* is less arched, and its legs are proportionally a bit longer. *Mesohippus*, like *Propalaeotherium,* was still a browser, but its low-crowned teeth were more efficient at grinding. During the coevolution of the early grasses and grazers, the skull of grazers became longer and larger as horses evolved longer teeth with thicker enamel, bigger jaws to place the teeth in, and larger muscles for chewing grass. Other herbivores also evolved mechanisms to digest the tough new grasses, including strong chewing teeth, several stomachs (in cud-chewing animals such as cattle and deer), and specialized gut bacteria. As we shall see in Section 5.4, the development of the savanna grasslands of Africa also had a significant effect on the course of primate evolution.

In the open savanna countryside there was nowhere to hide, so grazers such as horses and various other hoofed animals evolved taller and longer-legged species that were well adapted for running away from predators. Living in herds became common too, as herding allows group defence with relatively little expenditure of energy and it increases the chance of early warning of the approach of a predator.

- What is the main difference between the feet of today's horses and those of early horses such as *Propalaeotherium*?

- Today's horses have only a single-toed hoof in contact with the ground, and the side toes are reduced to insignificant splints (*Atlas* pp.138, 193), whereas early horses had more toes. *Propalaeotherium*, for example, had four toes on the front foot, and three toes on the hind foot (*Atlas*, p.133).

The story of horse evolution largely concerns an overall increase in size, with improvements in running ability and chewing capacity, but by no means has horse evolution been in a single straight line. Far from it: the evolutionary tree of horses has been a messy 'bush' with lots of genera and species, with many genera often living at the same time, and there have also been some size decreases. Today's only horse genus, *Equus*, is not the culmination of an inevitable trend, but merely the last surviving twig of a once extensive, sprawling bush. The box on the bottom of p.149 of the *Atlas* summarizes the last 11 000 years of horse history.

5.3.1 Riversleigh

Riversleigh, in Queensland, Australia is another World Heritage Site because of its remarkable fossil vertebrate faunas which span a long period — from the Miocene, 23 Ma ago, to less than 20 000 years ago. Carbonate-rich muds accumulated on the floor of shallow lakes in a lowland rainforest and subsequently formed hard limestones. The limestones were later dissolved by groundwater in places to form caves in which more recent bones accumulated, especially those of bats (placental mammals) which were able to fly to Australia by island hopping from Southeast Asia.

Now read the *Atlas*, pp.140–141. Note also that a fossil kangaroo jaw from Riversleigh is shown on p.139.

In mid Cretaceous times marsupials were one of the most successful groups of mammals and were spread throughout the Americas and Australia (Section 5.2). By late Cretaceous times, Australia was finally isolated from all the other continents as an ocean opened up between Australia and Antarctica.

- What was the effect of this isolation on the mammal fauna of Australia?

- The early mammals of Australia were dominated by marsupials, and when Australia became isolated they were effectively trapped in the continent. Unlike the Americas, there was no land bridge to allow the invasion of the more evolved placental mammals (*Atlas*, pp.140–141).

Eventually, some Australasian marsupials were made extinct by invading placentals such as the European fox, introduced by that most destructive of all placentals, the human. Today, we tend to think of plant-eating kangaroos and koalas as typical Australian marsupials. However, in Miocene times the Australian marsupials were much more diverse.

- Which Riversleigh marsupials filled the role of top land carnivores that today is mainly occupied by the big cats in the Americas, Africa and Asia?

- There was a cat-sized marsupial 'lion', *Priscileo*; a flesh-eating kangaroo (*Ekaltadeta*); and a marsupial 'tiger', called a thylacine. Note that the number of carnivores, however, was small enough to allow a variety of flightless birds to thrive (*Atlas*, pp.140–141).

- Which major component of the Riversleigh ecosystem is not generally preserved in the limestones?

- Plants (*Atlas*, pp.140–141).

- So how do we know that there were plants living in the area?

- There are fossils of various plant eaters, such as the cow-sized *Neohelos*, rat kangaroos and possums, indicating that much vegetation must have been present (*Atlas*, p.140).

The lake waters of the region were relatively rich in oxygen and the warm climates seem to have promoted the breakdown of plant tissues by microbes and soil-dwelling detritivores (detritus-eating organisms) such as millipedes. Consequently, the vegetation shown in the panorama on pp.140–141 of the *Atlas* is not named; it is reconstructed from contemporary fossils elsewhere.

Clearly, the reconstructions in the *Atlas* and elsewhere are based on presently available information and they approximate reality rather than actually represent it.

- Look briefly at the reconstruction of the Messel ecosystem on pp.132–133 of the *Atlas*, or the Riversleigh rainforest on pp.140–141. What is the most obvious reason why such busy-looking panoramas are not the equivalent of typical snapshots of the scene?

- It is most unlikely that so many individuals of different species of large animals would be in the same small area at exactly the same time: ask any wildlife photographer (even with remotely operated cameras) or explorer. Such illustrations are, however, useful for showing the life of the time in a naturalistic setting — a sort of pictorial zoological garden.

5.4 The emergence of humans

In 1619, the Italian philosopher, Lucilio Vanini, was burned alive for suggesting that humans originated from apes. Over two centuries later, Charles Darwin was so anxious about the implications of his theory of evolution for humans that all he said about it in the first edition of *On the Origin of Species* in 1859 was that 'light will be thrown on the origin of man and his history'. Darwin's cautionary approach to what he knew was a highly contentious subject was too much for many of his critics, some of whom immediately labelled the *Origin of Species* as the 'ape theory'. Anatomical similarities between us and the higher apes (such as the chimpanzees and orang-utan) had been known for a long time. Indeed, when the great Swedish biologist, Linnaeus (*Atlas G*, p.200), formally classified our own species as *Homo sapiens* ('wise man') in 1758, he placed the genus *Homo* within the Order Primates, which then, as now, also included apes, monkeys and lemurs. When he was criticized for doing so, Linnaeus challenged anyone to show any significant structural difference between humans and the other primates.

Homo sapiens is one of about 200 living species of primate (*Atlas G*, p.213). The Glossary entry and Figure 5.1 imply that primates first appeared in the early Tertiary, although some experts believe that they originated earlier, e.g. by the statement on p.107 of the *Atlas* that the late Cretaceous *Purgatorius* is the earliest primate.

Homo sapiens, all our extinct relatives in the genus *Homo*, and all the australopithecines, i.e. the extinct 'ape-man' genera *Australopithecus* and *Ardipithecus*, are collectively placed in a family called the **hominids** (*Atlas G*, p.209). Darwin was certainly right in his prediction that light would be thrown on human history: we now know that at least 15 hominid species have existed over the last 4 or 5 Ma. Some experts also place the 'higher' apes (chimps, gorilla and orang-utan) within the hominids.

Although living humans are widely dispersed around the globe and some groups have, until quite recently, been isolated geographically for many years, they can generally all interbreed and produce fertile young. We therefore belong to a single species — *Homo sapiens*. Analysis of DNA from living humans around the world shows a remarkable degree of genetic similarity.

As we proceed through the complex story of human evolution, you will find it useful to refer frequently to Figure 5.2, which summarizes the geological time ranges and probable evolutionary relationships of all the hominids mentioned. Bear in mind throughout this section that there is probably no more contentious area in palaeontology than the evolutionary relationships of hominids, and that the scheme presented here is but one of many you may see. Not only in other schemes do the inferred relationships between species often differ in detail, as do the species age ranges, but what one expert regards as two separate species may be considered a single species by another. And quite often the finding of a single new hominid fossil requires the existing evolutionary tree to be modified. In Figure 5.2, just some of the many uncertainties are indicated by question marks. There is, however, general agreement over the broad pattern in which a common stock gave rise to two main branches — a 'robust' line (including, for example, *Australopithecus robustus*) and a more lightly built 'gracile' line, from which *Homo* emerged.

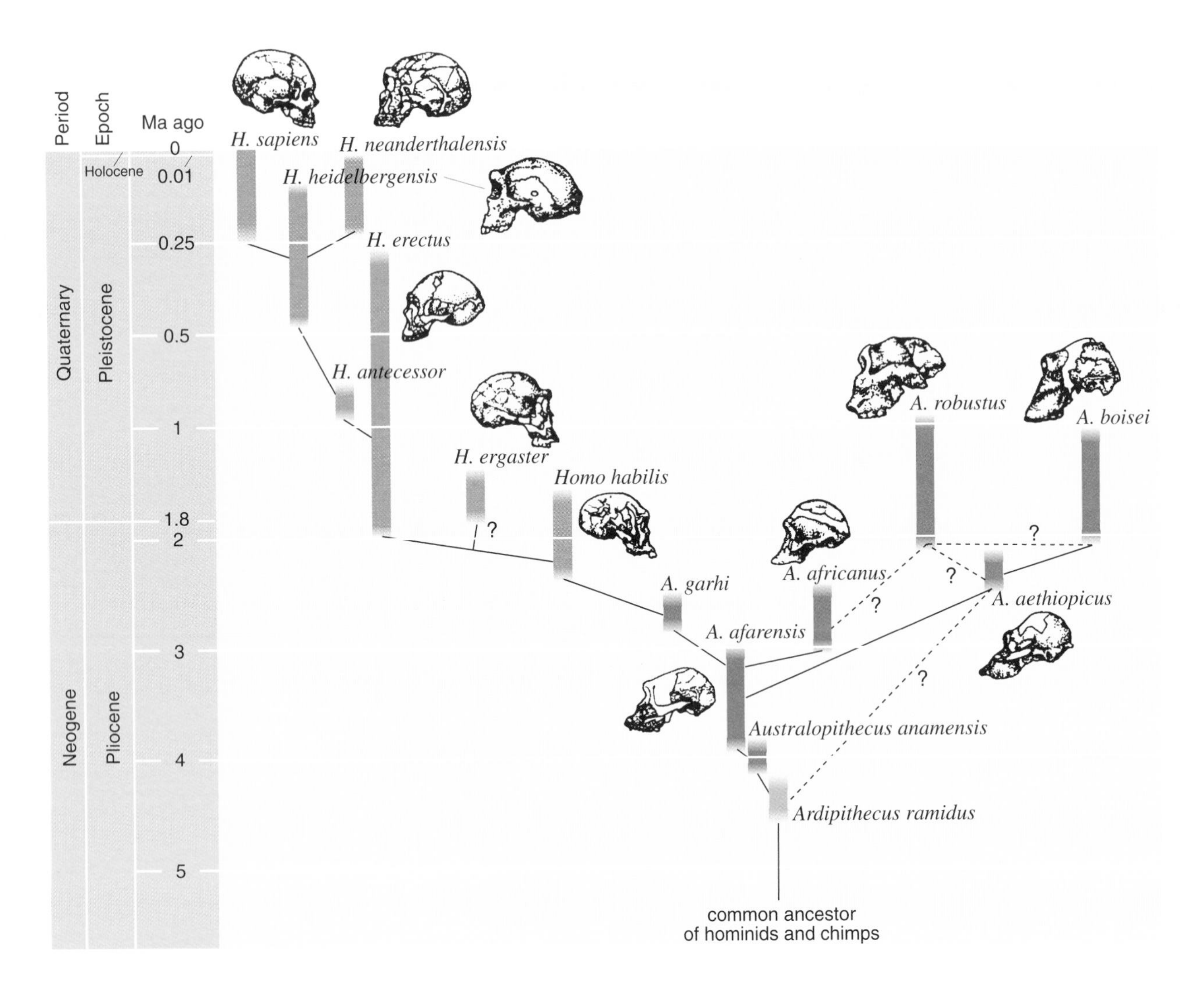

Figure 5.2 The geological time ranges and probable evolutionary relationships of hominids over the last 5 Ma.

The human 'family tree' is probably in reality more of a bush with many branches, only some of which have been discovered. Notice too from Figure 5.2 that, as with the evolution of horses (Section 5.3), hominid evolution has been far from a straight line. The arrangement of different species of *Homo* from left to right across pp.156–157 of the *Atlas*, each facing the same way, should not be misinterpreted as showing the 'Ascent of Man' on some predetermined path. Our species is, indeed, exceptional in many ways, not least for the potential we have to determine the fate of so many other species. But the notion that we are the pinnacle of evolutionary achievement — the result of continuous, inevitable progress — is one that finds no favour with evolutionary biologists today.

Question 5.2 What are the main reasons why it is often easier to establish the evolutionary relationships of, say, Palaeozoic trilobites or Mesozoic ammonites than those of hominids — even though our ancestors (most of who lived in the tropics) are much more recent and humans are not extinct? ◀

Piecing the whole jigsaw puzzle of human evolution together is exceedingly difficult. Fossil remains of extinct hominid species are incomplete and very rare, for the reasons discussed in Question 5.2: to date, only a few thousand fragmentary skeletons represent the sum total of our known extinct hominid relatives. Only teeth, large knuckle joints and bits of skull tend to be found. On this evidence, deciding how much morphological variation there was within a single species, i.e. where to place the species boundaries, is difficult and subjective. The fossil record of many other primates, e.g. chimpanzees, is even worse, especially if they have always lived in tropical forests, where decay of organic material, including bone, is normally rapid and complete.

Now read p.150 of the *Atlas*. There it states that the hominid ancestors of humans diverged from the other African apes only 4.5 Ma ago; more recent evidence, however, suggests that this occurred about 6.0 Ma ago.

- Place the following species in order of *decreasing* closeness of evolutionary relationship to us: common chimp; orang-utan; pygmy chimp; gorilla.
- Pygmy chimp (the most closely related); common chimp; gorilla; orang-utan (*Atlas*, p.150).
- What percentage difference is there between the DNA of chimps and humans?
- Less than 2% (*Atlas*, pp.150–151).

5.4.1 The first discoveries of early hominids

By the end of the nineteenth century, fragmentary skeletons had turned up in various European countries, mainly in caves and often associated with stones clearly modified for use as tools and weapons. Although many of the bones were generally similar to those of modern humans, some did show curious differences, such as having thick walls. Some skulls also had prominent bony brow ridges and virtually no forehead.

The first of these skeletal remains, found in 1856, came from a cave above the valley of the river Neander near Dusseldorf in Germany. Although the anatomical differences were accurately described at the time, they were not recognized for what they were — evidence of a separate human species. Instead, they were dismissed as the remains of a rickety cossack horseman or some pre-Roman savage race. But William King, a professor of geology in Ireland, recognized in 1864 that their anatomy was sufficiently different to warrant designation of the 'Neanderthaler' as a separate species, *Homo neanderthalensis*. This was the first of our ancient human relatives to be recognized as a different species and, as we now know, it was also the most recent human species to become extinct: Neanderthals died out a mere 30 000 years ago.

By the latter part of the nineteenth century, Darwin was arguing that because the chimp and gorilla are specific to Africa, that's where we were most likely to find fossils of our more ancient relatives. However, the German evolutionist Ernst Haeckel (*Atlas*, p.187) thought that the orang-utan of Southeast Asia was closer to humans and so our ancestors were more likely to be found there. In 1891, a Dutch doctor, Eugene Dubois, trying to prove Haeckel right, found some skeletal remains of what he called *Pithecanthropus erectus* (now known as *Homo erectus*) in Java (Southeast Asia). Although Dubois was right in thinking he had found a 'missing link' in human evolution, few others supported his conclusions; only some 30 years later was the significance of his find fully appreciated when similar fossils were found in China. It was not until the 1920s that fossil evidence to support Darwin's theory of an African origin began to emerge.

The first of the 'southern apes' (i.e. australopithecines, *Atlas*, p.205) was found in South Africa in 1924 and named as *Australopithecus africanus* by Raymond Dart (*Atlas*, p.199), but again it was many years before the significance of the find was generally accepted. The australopithecines were small (mostly 4 to 5 feet tall, 1.2 m to 1.5 m), upright-walking hominids which lived between 4.5 (or possibly as much as 6.0) and 1.0 Ma ago in Africa. Currently, about eight or nine australopithecine species are recognized. The later, more robust australopithecines, *Australopithecus aethiopicus, A. robustus* (*Atlas*, p.144) and *A. boisei*, are sometimes placed in a separate genus, *Paranthropus*. These australopithecines were contemporaries of the first members of the genus *Homo* from around 2.4 Ma ago until about 1.0 Ma ago and, although relatively long lived, left no descendants (Figure 5.2 and *Atlas*, pp.146–147).

The earliest known members of our genus *Homo* are placed in the species *Homo habilis*. Some experts consider there was also another contemporary species, *H. rudolfensis* (not shown separately in Figure 5.2). These earliest, most ancient humans dating from 2.4 Ma ago are thought to have evolved from the more slenderly built australopithecines, such as *A. garhi* or possibly *A. africanus* (Figure 5.2).

The most important early member of the genus *Homo* was the long-lived species *Homo erectus*, which survived from 1.9 Ma ago to about 300 000 years ago. There are recent claims that *Homo erectus* survived until somewhere between 53 000 and 27 000 years ago in Southeast Asia (not shown on Figure 5.2). As we have seen, *Homo erectus* had a very wide distribution, and remains dated as early as 1.8 Ma old have been found in the Caucasus region of Georgia. It is clear that some populations of *Homo erectus* must have migrated out of Africa very soon after the species originated, moving north sometime before 1.8 Ma ago. For some time the big question was what happened to those widespread *Homo erectus* populations in the end? Did they just die out, to be replaced much later by a wave of modern humans, or did they possibly evolve into more modern humans *independently* in separate populations spread across Europe, Africa and Asia? The latter idea is the so-called 'multiregional hypothesis', which now seems highly unlikely. There is, in contrast, strong evidence for the 'Out of Africa 2' model, i.e. that a second wave of migration out of Africa about 100 000 years ago was the source of all modern humans. In this model, all but one of the populations of *Homo erectus* (in Africa) died out completely without providing any further genes to more recent species of *Homo*. What little genetic variation there is within *Homo sapiens* is widest within the present African gene pool, and other non-African populations are all rather similar to each other, suggesting little time has elapsed since their divergence. The combined evidence suggests that all modern humans originated in a small population that lived in Africa some time between 450 000 and 130 000 years ago. Several other extinct species of *Homo* existed before modern humans (*H. sapiens*) evolved and their inter-relationships have been a matter of considerable debate.

Neanderthals (*Homo neanderthalensis*) seem to have had several morphological characters, including stocky bodies, that made them particularly well adapted to the intensely cold, harsh conditions of the late Pleistocene. The evidence from fragments of DNA recently recovered from Neanderthal bones shows no sign that today's European populations have inherited genes characteristic of Neanderthals, confirming that they were an independent species. The future recovery of DNA from other ancient members of the human family 'bush' will help resolve other major questions about hominid evolution. The analysis of DNA from the various living peoples of Asia, Australasia and the Pacific region is revealing the routes and timing of the dispersal of modern humans throughout these regions.

A very new development is the analysis of the ratios of carbon and nitrogen **isotopes** (*Atlas G*, p.210) in bone (and hair, where preserved) as indicators of feeding habits. Animals that predominantly eat plants have distinctive carbon and nitrogen isotope 'signatures' compared with meat eaters or omnivores. For instance, isotope analysis of hair from 'Otzi', the 5200 year old Neolithic Ice Man shows that he was practically vegan, with a diet based mainly on cereals. By comparison, the Neanderthals were predominantly meat eaters with very little plant food in their diet.

- Read the first two sentences at the top of p.147 of the *Atlas* and refer to Figure 5.2. What error in the *Atlas* needs correcting?

- The other hominid present with *Homo erectus* 800 000 years ago is *Homo antecessor*, not *Homo ergaster*.

The key points about hominid evolution are rather spread out in the *Atlas*. As you study the remaining pages there that relate to hominid evolution, work through Question 5.3 below, which will help you to put all the information on hominids here and in the *Atlas* in perspective. The relevant pages in the *Atlas* are pp.144–145; 146–147; 151; 156–157.

Question 5.3 The following paragraphs, once complete, will act as a useful summary of many important aspects. Write in the missing numbered items as you read through the relevant pages of the *Atlas*. Alternatively, you may wish to use this as a test of your understanding afterwards. Note that not every hominid species shown in Figure 5.2 and mentioned in the *Atlas* is included here.

On the evidence of genetic similarity, the most closely related primate species to us is the .... (1). We shared a common ancestor with all the Old World monkeys of Africa, Asia and Europe around .... (2) Ma ago, and with chimps about 6.0 Ma ago. The earliest known confirmed hominid species, the first of a succession of .... (3) (i.e. 'southern apes') is *Ardipithecus* .... (4), which appeared around 4.5 Ma ago. This species walked upright and lived in a woodland habitat. Spectacular footprints (trace fossils) of the later *Australopithecus* .... (5) are preserved in volcanic ash from Laetoli, Tanzania and reveal that by 3.6 Ma ago hominids were certainly walking fully upright (though not in exactly the same fashion as us). The skeleton of 'Lucy' from Ethiopia is a famous body fossil of this species. A later species, *Australopithecus garhi*, first described from Ethiopia in 1999, lived in open grasslands around a lake with abundant game about .... (6) Ma ago. The shift to meat-eating and first use of stone tools which occurred around this time roughly coincided with the emergence of the genus .... (7).

The earliest known members of our genus lived in Africa from about 2.4 Ma to 1.6 Ma ago and are called *Homo* .... (8) ('handy-man'); these had a bigger brain capacity than any of the australopithecines. Another species found in the fossiliferous deposits around Lake Turkana in Kenya (among other places), is the long-legged and taller *Homo* .... (9) ('upright human'), which appeared in Africa about 1.9 Ma ago. Its brain capacity had reached 1.0 litres (1000 ml) by about 1.0 Ma ago and rose to 1.3 litres by 500 000 years ago. For comparison, modern humans have a brain capacity of about .... (10) litres. *Homo erectus* was particularly successful and was the first hominid to migrate out of Africa. Some populations of *Homo erectus* migrated out of Africa very soon after the species originated, moving north sometime before .... (11) Ma ago. Fossils of *Homo erectus*, along with stone tools, have been found throughout much of Europe and as far afield as China (so-called 'Peking Man') and Java ('Java Man'). The stone tools made by *Homo erectus* include Oldowan flakes and chopping tools in Africa (named after Olduvai Gorge in Tanzania, where they were first found by Louis and Mary Leakey (*Atlas*, p.200) in the 1950s), and .... (12) hand axes in Europe.

Modern humans, *Homo* .... (13), first appeared in Africa, probably about 200 000 years ago (though estimates range from about 450 000 years ago to 130 000 years ago). We spread throughout Africa and then, like the migration of *Homo erectus* nearly 2 Ma earlier, spread further north about 100 000 years ago: 'Out of Africa 2'. We reached the Middle East (today's Israel) by 90 000 years ago and fanned out east and west, reaching the Far East by about 60 000 years ago and the far west of Europe by around .... (14) years ago. In Europe modern humans found the territory already occupied by another human species, the heavily built, stocky Neanderthals, *Homo* .... (15). The Neanderthals, which ranged in age from 200 000 to .... (16) years ago, buried their dead, made tools and weapons, and even had a bigger brain (on average) than *Homo sapiens*.

DNA evidence suggests that Neanderthals and modern humans diverged at least ....(17) years ago. The common ancestor of both *Homo sapiens* and Neanderthals may well have been *Homo* .... (18), which in turn may have evolved from *Homo erectus* in Africa via an intermediate *Homo* .... (19), which lived about 1.0–0.8 Ma ago. This part of the human evolutionary story is, however, still hotly disputed by the experts. Despite coexisting in Europe for about 10 000 years, Neanderthals and modern humans rarely interbred, if at all. The earliest *Homo sapiens* to reach Europe (40 000 years ago) are called .... (20). Taller, and more slender boned than Neanderthals, they left many paintings and sculptures in European caves.

Recent dating of Australian finds suggests that modern humans might have reached Australia as early as 60 000 years ago. Colonization of the Americas was last, and depended on the formation of the .... (21) between Siberia and Alaska as a result of lowered sea level during the Quaternary .... (22). This probably allowed modern humans and other animals to cross from Asia into North America some .... (23) years ago. The earliest distinct culture in the Americas, about 11 500 years old, is characterized by razor-sharp stone spearheads, and is called the .... (24) culture. ◀

Question 5.4 Assuming *Homo sapiens* originated about 200 000 years ago, for what percentage of the time since life began has our species existed? ◀

The fossil record has only a limited potential for recording the spectrum of early human nature and activities. Just where does the 'glass floor' to humanity lie — in other words when did our ancient relatives become truly human? This is a difficult question, hinging on the criterion — or criteria — taken to define humanity. What would you choose — language, bipedalism, culture, intelligence, tool-making, being fully self-conscious and aware of one's mortality, a capacity for religion, or having a sense of humour? Is it some other criterion or a combination of all of these? We finish this section leaving you to ponder this question.

5.5 The Quaternary Period

As we saw on p.144 of the *Atlas* (Section 5.4), the late Tertiary climate was characterized by fluctuating temperatures and humidity in a context of long-term global cooling. The Antarctic ice sheet around the South Pole was already well established by the time extensive ice sheets began to develop in the Northern Hemisphere during a major cooling event 2.6 Ma ago. Ice sheets were more widely developed in the Northern Hemisphere than the Southern Hemisphere because of the more extensive land masses around the North Pole (*Atlas*, p.152).

In the last 2.6 million years there have been numerous fluctuations in climate, though during this period the globe has been in an 'icehouse state' (*Atlas G*, p.210) — colder, on average, than at any time during the last 250 million years. Sometimes, however, during the Quaternary Ice Age it was significantly *warmer* than today: about 125 000 years ago, during the last interglacial, mean annual temperatures in Britain were at least 2 °C higher. Remains of *Hippopotamus amphibius*, the same species as the common hippopotamus living in Africa today, have been found in river gravels of this age in London, East Anglia and as far north as Darlington.

As is shown in the diagram on p.164 of the *Atlas*, the Quaternary Period is itself divided into two epochs, the Pleistocene, which began 1.8 Ma ago, and the Holocene (or Recent), which began 10 000 years ago and continues to the present day. The boundary between the Pleistocene and Holocene is chosen as 10 000 years ago because it was about then that a major thaw occurred, taking no more than about 15–50 years. Since this sudden warming up, the Earth's climate has been more stable than during any other 10 000-year interval in at least the last 200 000 years.

Figure 5.3 shows just some of the many species which can be found as fossils in late Pliocene and early Pleistocene British sediments and whose appearance heralded the onset of major glaciation; today, these same species live only in Arctic conditions.

(a)

(b)

(c)

Figure 5.3 Three mollusc species found in late Pliocene and early Pleistocene deposits of East Anglia that today live only in Arctic conditions. (a) The bivalve *Astarte borealis* (4 cm); (b) the bivalve *Macoma calcarea* (3.5 cm); (c) the gastropod *Epitonium greenlandicum* (3 cm).

The causes and effects of the Quaternary Ice Age, and of the alternations of climate within it, are many and complex — and still much debated — and we need not discuss the issues in depth here. Changes in the configuration of continents and alterations to the pattern of seawater and air currents are just some of the many influences affecting climate. To give just one example, we saw in Section 5.2.1 that by 3 Ma ago, the Panama seaway between North and South America had closed and the land bridge linking these two continents (the Isthmus of Panama) was firmly in place, with important consequences for life and for climate. As explained on p.153 of the *Atlas*, warm Atlantic water was no longer able to flow around the Equator but was instead diverted northwards. This in turn led to increased precipitation at high latitudes which eventually fed the accumulation of ice sheets on land in eastern Canada, Greenland and Scandinavia. At times during the Quaternary Ice Age, the Gulf Stream may have shut down, so that northwest Europe may have no longer been bathed in the flow of relatively warm seawater and air that the Gulf Stream brings it today. The Earth's climate system is, of course, immensely complex, and involves many feedbacks. A feedback occurs when a change in one variable (e.g. the percentage of land covered by snow and ice) leads to a change in another variable (e.g. the percentage of the Sun's heat energy reflected back into space), and that change then leads to a further change in the original variable.

With growing concern over probable **global warming** due to the increase in atmospheric carbon dioxide (CO_2) released by burning fossil fuels, 'the past is the key to the future' has become an important concept. Predicting future environmental changes can only be possible if we know what happened in the past, *and why*. Fossils have a major part to play in this endeavour because of their ability to record environmental change. Among the most important types of fossils used to analyse Quaternary climate change are pollen grains (Figure 1.3) and insect remains, especially beetles. The geographical distribution of individual species of plants and insects today is often very sensitive to climatic factors. Many beetles, for example, are adapted to a very narrow temperature range, and during climatic fluctuations species tend to migrate north and south, following the movements of climatic belts, tracking closely their preferred conditions, and often undergoing little or no evolutionary change.

Detailed evidence for climate change throughout the last few million years has come primarily from analysing the composition of fossil forams, chambered marine creatures mostly less than 1 mm across (*Atlas*, p.153). The shells of these organisms, common in ocean floor sediments, are made of calcium carbonate and contain varying proportions of two oxygen isotopes. By measuring changes in the ratio of one oxygen isotope to the other in shells from successive strata it is possible to obtain an indirect estimate of changes in temperature over that period. The climate record over the last 420 000 years or so is also supplemented by isotope and other compositional data derived from ice cores drilled through layers of snow and ice accumulated at the poles (*Atlas*, p.158).

For much of the last 2 Ma, Britain was connected to mainland Europe, but rising sea levels after the big thaw of ice sheets and glaciers around the end of the Pleistocene broke this connection about 8000 years ago. Note that the melting of ice floating in the sea does not itself produce a rise in sea level. You can easily conduct an experiment to show this. Place some ice cubes in a glass of water and fill it precisely to the brim with water (the ice cubes will stick up a bit above that level). The glass will not overflow when the ice cubes melt: the water level stays the same. Global sea levels will only rise as a result of ice melting if that ice has been water taken out of the sea and temporarily 'locked up' as snow and ice on land.

During glaciations, the weight of the ice sheets (up to about 3 km thick) is so great that the land surface underneath is pushed downwards. When this weight is removed, the land surface rebounds, but at a much slower rate than sea-level rise (see photo in *Atlas*, p.158). Parts of the Highlands of Scotland, for instance, are rising today by about 3 mm per year as a result of this post-glacial rebound.

Box 5.1 Mammoths

Mammoths were elephants that had evolved adaptations to the cold climates of the Quaternary Ice Age. Among these adaptations were long hair, a short tail and small ears to minimize frostbite. The coarse, wiry outer hairs of a woolly mammoth were about six times thicker than a typical human hair; their orange colour today is probably not natural but the result of pigment change during long burial. Below this coarse hair was a dense layer of short, fine hairs. Contrary to popular belief, mammoths did not live in a habitat dominated by ice and snow, but rather the cold steppe environment beyond the ice sheets as described in the *Atlas*, pp.154–155. Another misconception is that all mammoths were 'mammoth' in size: although a typical woolly mammoth stood at just over 3 m in height, some species, such as one that lived on islands off California, were only about 1.2 m high at the shoulder.

Mammoth cheek teeth (molars) and tusks (greatly enlarged upper incisors) are quite common fossils in Pleistocene gravels. Mammoths got through six sets of teeth during a full lifetime. Look at the three woolly mammoth cheek teeth pictured on p.153 of the *Atlas*. The smallest of these, no bigger than a human molar, is the first molar with which the animal was born. The third in the series is shown top left, and the sixth, top right, is over 30 cm long and weighs about 2 kg. These teeth are upper molars, and the biting surfaces that were in contact with the food are the slightly convex, ridged surfaces to the bottom left of each tooth shown. The biting surface of lower molars, such as those visible in Figure 5.4, are slightly concave. Only a small part of the height of the tooth (about 2 cm in larger teeth) projected above the gum.

When eating, powerful muscles moved the mammoth jaw back and forth (rather than from side to side as in cattle). This caused the sharp enamel ridges crossing both the upper and lower molars to grind past each other, breaking up the food between them. Only one tooth was fully in operation at any one time in each of the four jaw areas (upper and lower, left and right). As each tooth wore out, it was replaced from behind by another tooth brought gradually into place by a sort of conveyor belt system, the process being repeated five times. This contrasts with humans, where each tooth is changed once (in childhood), and the replacement grows from below. The mammoth's vegetarian diet was mainly grasses, sedges and occasional herbs, although hundreds of plant types have been identified in the stomachs of frozen individuals. They may have spent up to 20 hours a day fuelling their great bulk. In some mammoths which lived at least 60 years, the sixth (i.e. final) molars are worn down so much that death may have been caused by an inability to chew.

The relative influence of human predation and climate change on the extinction of mammoths was discussed earlier in Section 3.10.2. The very last mammoths were members of a woolly mammoth population with a small body size (only 1.8 m tall) that died out on the remote Wrangel Island, north of Siberia, only 3800 years ago — about 700 years after the Great Pyramid was built in Egypt.

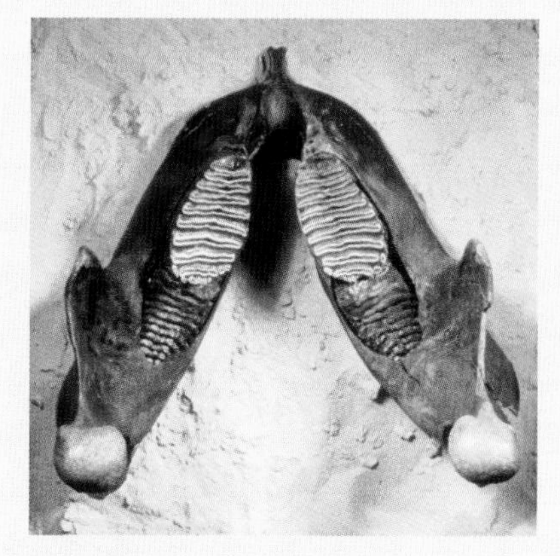

Figure 5.4 Lower jaw of a woolly mammoth, *Mammuthus primigenius*, from Condover, Shropshire, about 12 500 years old. The jaw is 60 cm wide.

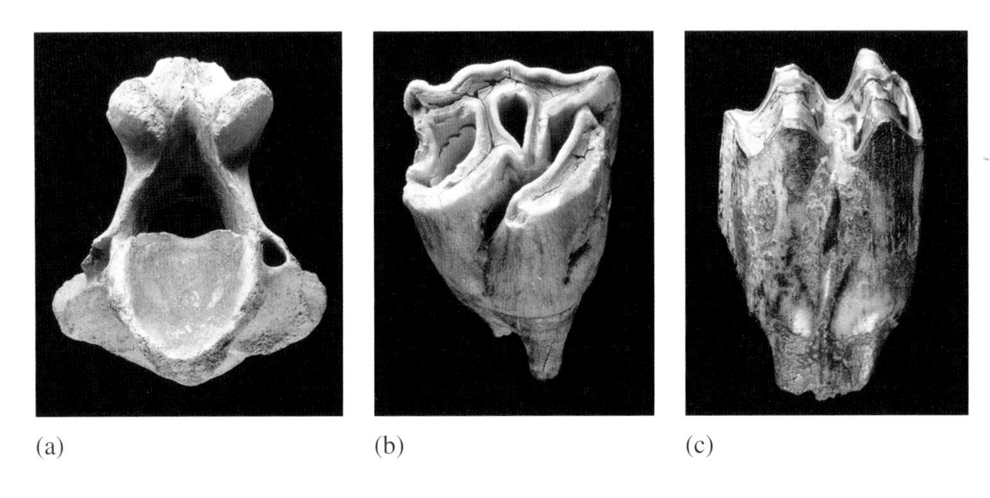

Figure 5.5 A variety of vertebrate fossils found in Pleistocene sediments near Cambridge. (a) Vertebra of an unknown species of rhinoceros (this is the second vertebra behind the head, the axis) (17 cm). (b) Cheek tooth of woolly rhinoceros, *Coelodonta antiquitatis* (6 cm). (c) Cheek tooth of aurochs or wild ox, *Bos primigenius*, the wild ancestor to modern domestic cattle, which became restricted to central Europe within the last 2000 years and was hunted to final extinction in Poland in AD 1627 (7 cm).

Figure 5.5 shows various vertebrate fossils that can be found in addition to occasional mammoth teeth in Pleistocene sands and gravels about 40 000 years old near Cambridge. When these sediments were deposited (and in general during the time between about 74 000 and 30 000 years ago), there was very little ice over lowland Britain, though there were glaciers further north. Continental weather systems dominated at this time; air was coming off the main European continent with little precipitation in it — a situation similar to the Siberian areas of steppe–tundra vegetation and permafrost today. There was, however, sufficient winter snowfall for spring and summer meltwaters to run rapidly off over the permanently frozen ground just below, carrying any sediment (including bones and teeth) they could pick up, and depositing the material when the current strength dropped sufficiently. It is important to realize that durable remains such as large bones and teeth may get 'reworked' by such processes many times, so that fossils from several different glacial and interglacial stages can get incorporated into the same layer, giving apparently conflicting evidence of climate. The time when the sediments were laid down is thus the *minimum* age of the fossils they contain; the more abraded the fossil, the more likely that it has been reworked from older deposits.

Now read the *Atlas*, pp.152–155, and pp. 158–159.

Question 5.5 You should answer this question after reading the above pages in the *Atlas*. Which of the following items (a) to (f), summarizing some aspects of the Quaternary Ice Age, are correct and which are incorrect? If any item is incorrect, what is wrong with it?

(a) The Quaternary Ice Age has been the only Ice Age in Earth history.

(b) During the Quaternary Ice Age, relatively long, cold 'glacials' alternated with much shorter, warmer 'interglacials'. We may be living within an interglacial at present, and if the pattern of past climatic change continues, another glacial may be due within the next few thousand years.

(c) The mammoth teeth occasionally trawled up by fishing boats from the bottom of the North Sea generally got there by dropping into the sea off melting icebergs.

(d) At the peak of the Quaternary Ice Age about 5% of all water at the Earth's surface became frozen and sea levels fell by about 10 m.

(e) Falling sea levels associated with glaciation meant that shallow seas became dry plains, and land bridges formed, connecting previously isolated islands to larger areas (such as the British Isles to Europe) and continents to continents (such as Asia to the Americas). This allowed the migration of many land-dwelling organisms, including humans, into newly available territories.

(f) The melting of ice sheets and glaciers releases huge volumes of glacial meltwater and sediment. Natural dams made of rock and ice holding back meltwaters sometimes collapse, causing locally catastrophic deluges. This is the origin of channelled scablands (*Atlas G*, p.214), such as those of Washington State in the USA. ◀

In general, despite the dramatic changes in climate, there was surprisingly little extinction of marine species (e.g. molluscs) during the Pleistocene, and the same is also true of plants and invertebrates (e.g. beetles) living on land. Extinction rates increased to a fairly minor extent in various groups as cooling intensified in the late Pliocene and early Pleistocene, but those species that survived the first climatic onslaughts proved well suited to withstand subsequent ones. Interestingly, there seems to have been relatively little evolution within species, especially marine invertebrates, subjected to these severe environmental changes. It may be that wide fluctuations in the physical environment over geological timescales tend to have the effect of keeping species relatively static in their morphology, and such species become more or less inert to environmental twists and turns.

As we saw in Section 3.10.2, many large mammals and large flightless birds became extinct between 15 000 and 10 000 years ago, and the evidence suggests that human hunting activities, as well as climate changes, were responsible. Although the legacy left by the Quaternary Ice Age forms the basis of much of the topography and wildlife of areas such as northern Europe, the extent to which landscapes and habitats have been modified by continuing human activities such as agriculture, urban development and industrialization cannot be overestimated. As we saw earlier, if current trends continue, the present time in Earth history could appear as another mass extinction in the geological record — 'the Sixth Extinction' to add to the previous Big Five. Prehistoric populations of humans could not have foreseen the eventual consequences of their actions but we ought to be able to do so: after all, we did call ourselves *Homo sapiens*.

5.6 Summary of Cenozoic life

The Cenozoic Era began with parts of the biosphere recovering from the end Cretaceous mass extinction. Gone forever were groups such as ammonites, belemnites, ichthyosaurs, and mosasaurs from the seas; dinosaurs from the land, and pterosaurs from the skies. These extinctions re-set the evolutionary stage, providing opportunities for groups that had been more or less waiting in the wings during the Mesozoic Era — especially the flowering plants, insects, snakes, birds and mammals. All these groups greatly increased in diversity during the Cenozoic.

The evolutionary radiation of mammals in the early Cenozoic led to groups adapted to a huge range of modes of life and environments. Some, for example, took to the sea (e.g. whales) while others took to the air (bats). The most detailed evidence of Cenozoic mammals and their ecosystems comes from sites with exceptionally well-preserved fossils such as Messel (Eocene) and Riversleigh (Miocene to Pleistocene). For most of the Cenozoic, when marsupial mammals were far more diverse than

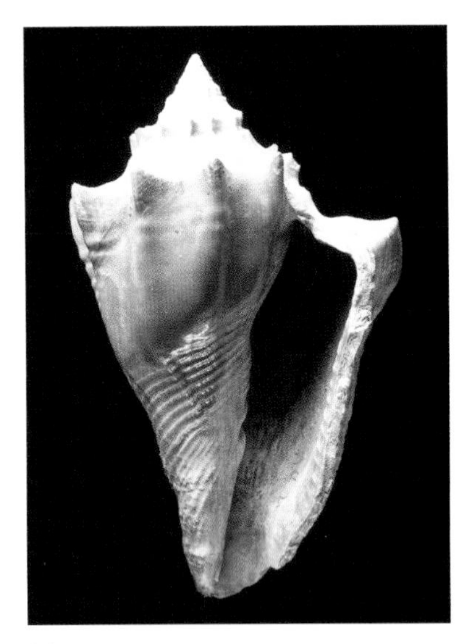

(a)

(b)

Figure 5.6 Palaeogene gastropods from southern England. (a) *Volutospina luctator* (9 cm); (b) *Theodoxus planulatus*, still showing the patterns of colour banding after about 35 Ma. The colour itself has probably altered. The largest shell is 9 mm long.

today, the mammal faunas of North and South America were isolated from each other by a seaway. The formation of the Central American land bridge about 3 Ma ago allowed extensive interchange of mammal species, some going south, some north, resulting in many extinctions. In Australia, where marsupials dominated, there was no land bridge to allow the invasion of the more evolved placental mammals. Eventually, some Australasian marsupials were made extinct by invading placentals — humans and the other placentals they introduced.

As landscapes became increasingly coloured by a kaleidoscopic palette of flowering plants, from tiny annual weeds to huge trees, many insects, birds and other animals evolved adaptations to match those of specific plants, whilst others were more generalist feeders. The payoff to the flowering plants for snacks of nectar they offered to insects was assistance in pollination. Larger animals, especially birds and the newly evolved mammals, ranging from primates to fruit-eating bats, played their part in distributing seeds from fruits and nuts.

Overall, a casual time traveller equipped to observe above and below water would probably notice more changes to life on land than to life in the sea through the Cenozoic. Changes to marine life included a massive increase in the diversity of bony fishes, as well as a proliferation of marine mammals. As far as marine invertebrates are concerned, gastropods (Figure 5.6) underwent a spectacular surge in diversity, and other examples of groups that diversified considerably include bivalves, reef-building scleractinian corals and echinoids, whilst the brachiopods never recovered their Mesozoic abundance.

The evolution of grasses (a group of flowering plants) in the mid Tertiary had far-reaching effects on animal life. Forests were replaced on many continents by open savanna grasslands, favouring grazers over browsers. The evolution of horses, for example, was strongly influenced by these changes in vegetation: they underwent an overall increase in size (though with exceptions), with improvements in running ability and chewing capacity.

As with the evolution of horses, hominid evolution has been far from a simple story of steady, straight-line change. Our species, *Homo sapiens*, and other hominids shared a common ancestor with the Old World monkeys of Africa, Asia and Europe around 28 Ma ago, and with chimpanzees about 6 Ma ago. The earliest known confirmed hominid species, *Ardipithecus ramidus*, the first of a succession of australopithecines, appeared around 4.5 Ma ago; it walked upright and lived in woods. The shift to meat-eating and the first use of stone tools occurred around 2.5 Ma. The earliest known members of our genus, *Homo habilis,* lived in Africa from about 2.4 to 1.6 Ma ago. The larger brained, taller *Homo erectus*, which appeared in Africa about 1.9 Ma ago, was particularly successful and long-ranging in time; it migrated northwards out of Africa sometime before 1.8 Ma ago, spreading into Europe and as far as China and Java. Around this time there were at least five hominid species in Africa.

Modern humans first evolved in Africa probably about 200 000 years ago (though estimates vary). We spread throughout Africa and then, like the migration of *Homo erectus* nearly 2 Ma earlier, spread further north about 100 000 years ago ('Out of Africa 2'), probably reaching the Far East and Australia by 60 000 years ago and the far west of Europe by around 40 000 years ago. The earliest *Homo sapiens* to reach Europe, called Cro-Magnons, found the territory already occupied by a more heavily built, stockier species — *Homo neanderthalensis*, which ranged in age from 200 000 to 30 000 years ago. These Neanderthals had, on average, a bigger brain than *Homo sapiens*.

During the last 2.6 million years, the globe has been in an 'icehouse state' — colder, on average, than at any time during the last 250 million years. Sometimes, however, during the numerous fluctuations of the Quaternary Ice Age it was significantly warmer than today. The build-up of ice on land caused global sea levels to fall by as much as 120 m, allowing the migration of many land-dwelling organisms into previously unavailable territories. For example, the colonization of the Americas by *Homo sapiens*, about 30 000 years ago, depended on the formation of the Bering land bridge between Siberia and Alaska as a result of lowered sea level at that time. Mammoths, which were cold-adapted elephants, lived with a variety of other hardy animals and plants in the areas of cold savanna areas or steppe adjacent to the ice sheets.

The Quaternary Period is itself divided into two epochs, the Pleistocene, which began 1.8 Ma ago, and the Holocene (or Recent), which began 10 000 years ago and continues to the present day. About 10 000 years ago there was a major thaw which happened with remarkable rapidity, probably within about 15–50 years. Since then the Earth's climate has been more stable than during any other 10 000-year interval in at least the last 200 000 years.

Among the fossils most often used to reveal details of Quaternary climate change are pollen grains, beetle remains, and forams. Despite the climatic upheavals, few groups suffered much extinction during the Pleistocene, the main exception being the many large mammals and large flightless birds that became extinct between 15 000 and 10 000 years ago, for which human hunting, as well as climate changes, seem responsible. Since then humans have wreaked ever-increasing disturbance on landscapes and their wildlife — indeed we have affected to some extent every part of the biosphere — and if current trends continue, this present time in Earth history could appear as another mass extinction in the geological record.

5.7 Perspective on the history of life

Having arrived at the present day after travelling through geological time, we now need to put into perspective what we've seen along the way.

This would be a very good time to read again, in quick succession, the four summaries at the end of Sections 2, 3 and 4, followed by the summary above in Section 5.6. Then read the *Atlas*, p.164 from the heading 'The earliest fossil remains' to the end of p.165. The summary chart on p.164 is particularly useful as it shows when various major groups first appeared.

You will have noticed that the *Atlas* tends to focus on certain groups of organisms at the expense of others. For example, vertebrates feature more than invertebrates and plants, and larger organisms feature far more than small ones. This reflects the strong tendency for most humans to be more interested in, say, mammals and birds than molluscs or bryozoans. Yet, as far as the fossil record is concerned, invertebrates, especially marine ones, are much more abundant in the fossil record than vertebrates (Section 1.2).

The organisms that most readily capture human attention are easily visible, intelligent animals with complex behaviour, such as mammals and birds. Warm, cuddly, mammals that most resemble human babies such as koala bears are especially popular. On the other hand, being a dangerous predator also gives an animal added interest. The natural fascination of children for vicious predators such as crocodiles, tigers, snakes and poisonous spiders is probably an expression of the innate predisposition humans have to learn about the limits of the environment, a characteristic which obviously benefited our ancestors. There is huge survival value in being both curious about, and fearful of, predators. Today, however, the threats to life from large, non-human predators have become minimal or even non-existent for many humans. In Europe, for example, our ancestors removed the threat of animals such as sabre-toothed tigers and various species of bear. But the natural predisposition to learn about predators remains, fuelling a horrified fascination even with animals no human ever knew, such as *Tyrannosaurus rex*, the resurrection of which remains extremely unlikely, despite the best endeavours of film-makers. But who knows, however, where our accelerating forays into genetic manipulation will end?

Evolving life has itself profoundly influenced conditions at the Earth's surface. For example, it was the photosynthetic activity of cyanobacteria that eventually converted an atmosphere lacking oxygen to one rich in it. Despite the potential, in theory, for catastrophic environmental changes to eliminate all forms of life (except perhaps extremophile bacteria), conditions have remained within sufficiently narrow limits for an enormous diversity of organisms to thrive and prosper. For example, for reasons that are not yet fully understood, the Earth's average surface temperature, currently 15 °C, is estimated to have remained between 5 °C and 20 °C for over 3 billion years. Despite the setbacks of extinctions, life in some form has persisted for nearly 4 billion years; there have always been sufficient winners to keep going the risky game of life.

All the available evidence suggests that by the beginning of the Quaternary, nearly 2 Ma ago, there was a greater diversity of life, and a higher total number of species, than ever before in Earth's history. The evidence for this is particularly strong for skeletonized marine invertebrates. We don't know, however, how many species exist today: estimates range from about 5 to 30 million. As we saw in Section 3.10.2, conservative estimates of current total extinction rates due to human activity are 5–50 species per day. The only groups that seem, on the whole, to be successfully fighting back against both intended and unintended extermination are microbes — especially viruses, bacteria and fungi. Because of their extremely short generation times and overall resilience, these groups continue to evolve apace, sometimes taking just a few hours to evolve new strains, as hospital pathologists will testify. Bacteria were the first organisms, and in many ways they remain the most successful ones. Morphological complexity, including higher intelligence, does not mean an organism is better adapted to its environment. In terms of sustained survival and reproduction, the bacteria in the soil are just as well — if not better — adapted to it as is the earthworm or the mole.

The fossil record will no doubt continue to surprise and excite us as new finds turn up in the decades and centuries to come. Palaeontology is one of the few sciences left where amateurs, and ordinary members of the public, including children, often make significant discoveries. In the next and final section, we give you some tips on finding fossils for yourself and making the most of the treasury of information they have to offer.

5.8 Collecting and studying fossils for yourself

Collecting fossils is, for many people, including children, an enjoyable, inexpensive and intellectually stimulating pursuit. Breaking open an ancient rock and realizing you're the first human ever to see the remains of the once-living organisms inside can be inspirational, even if the fossils are as mundane as bivalves or snails. There is no faster way of learning about common fossils than to collect and study them yourself. Fossils form a major scientific, educational and recreational resource, and are part of any country's heritage. This resource is, however, finite and only a responsible approach to fossil hunting will ensure that it remains viable for future generations to enjoy. Collect only a few representative specimens and, unless you have time to make a detailed scientific study of fossils *in situ* and publish your findings, obtain them from fallen or loose material where possible. Encourage responsible collecting in others too.

The main skill required in fossil collecting is the ability to distinguish patterns in rocks that indicate evidence of an organism, as opposed to the many, less organized, inorganic shapes that result from weathering, fracture, original sedimentary structures (e.g. ripples), and so on. Some people have an innate gift for spotting fossils, but the joint skills of collection *and* identification can soon be acquired with practice and by familiarization with the shapes and cross-sections that different groups of fossils display when partially embedded in rocks.

Where to look

Fossils can be collected in most places where sedimentary rocks of Cambrian age and younger are exposed at the Earth's surface. Clays, shales and limestones tend to be more richly fossiliferous than sandstones, though the latter may yield abundant trace fossils. Figure 5.7 overleaf shows a simplified geological map of the British Isles, the rocks of which are remarkably varied. The different colours show where rocks of particular ages (or origin in the case of igneous rocks) occur either at the surface or below the soil. You can, for example, use the map and its key to find out the approximate age and type of rock in the area where you live or where you are going to visit. Much more detailed geological maps, made and published by the British Geological Survey, are available and are indispensable for quickly getting to grips with the geology of local areas.

As you can see from Figure 5.7, rocks tend to be youngest in the southeast of Britain and generally become older to the west and north. Note particularly the broad, roughly parallel bands of Carboniferous, Permian, Mesozoic and Cenozoic strata crossing central, eastern and southern England. Older, Palaeozoic rocks outcrop at the surface in southwest and northern England, Wales, Ireland and southern Scotland. Further north still, relationships between rocks of different ages become more complex, but rocks there too generally become older the further northwest you travel.

Some of the best places to look for fossils are coastlines where erosion is continually exposing fresh rock surfaces, and waves and currents turn over pebbles. In such situations fossils can be lost forever unless collected. Where access is possible, working quarries can also be fruitful, though today many fossils that would have been seen and kept by quarry workers in less mechanized times go totally undetected, obliterated in the crushing plant. Similarly, road cuttings may be productive, if access is both permitted and safe.

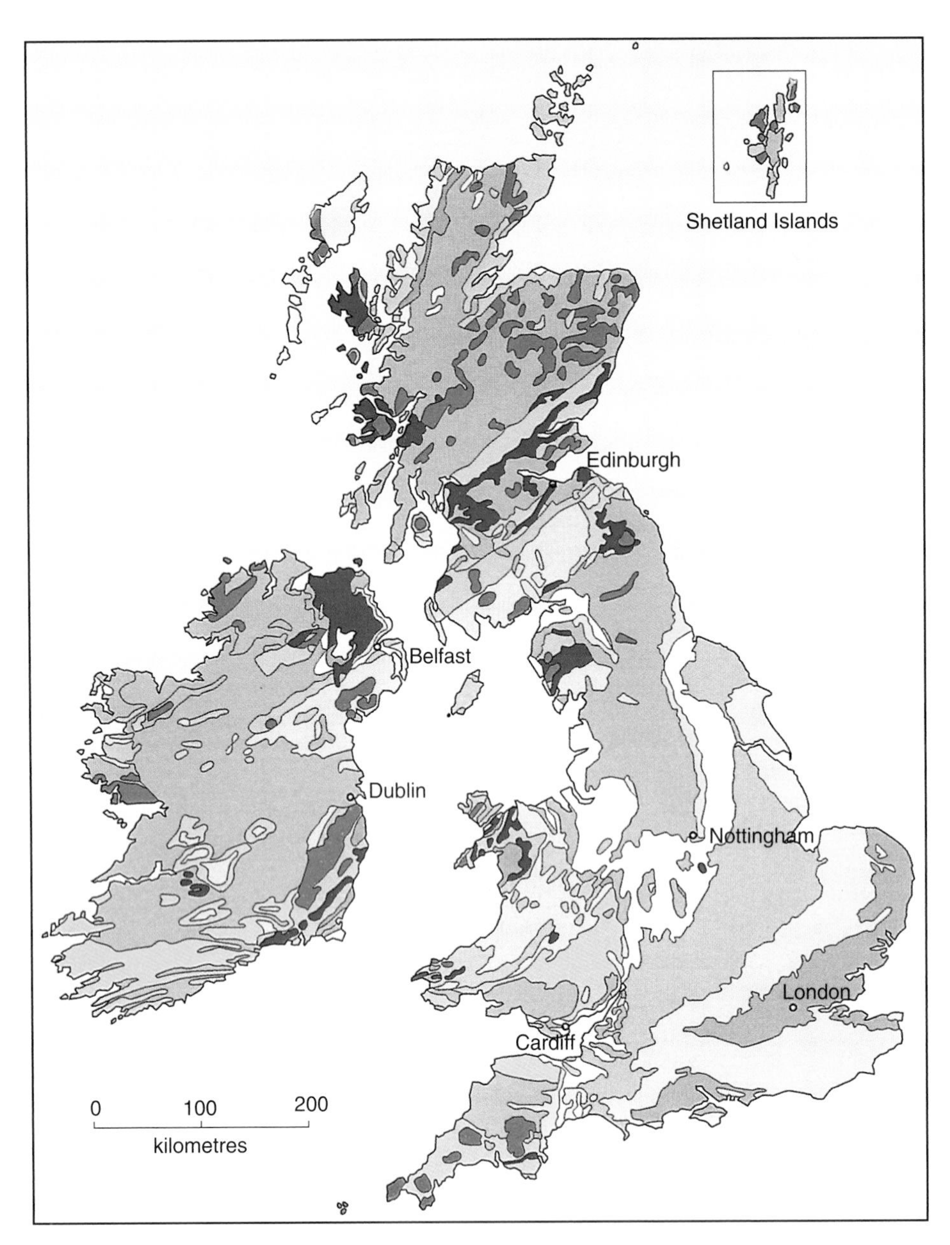

SEDIMENTARY ROCKS

CENOZOIC

Rock	Description	Age
Tertiary and marine early Quaternary	mainly clays and sands; Quaternary glacial deposits not shown	up to 65

MESOZOIC

Rock	Description	Age
Cretaceous	mainly chalk, clays and sands	65–142
Jurassic	mainly limestones and clays	142–206
Triassic	mudstones, sandstones and conglomerates	206–248

PALAEOZOIC

Rock	Description	Age
Permian	mainly limestones, mudstones and sandstones	248–290
Carboniferous	limestones, sandstones, shales and coal seams	290–354
Devonian	sandstones, shales, conglomerates; slates and limestones	354–417

PALAEOZOIC continued

Rock	Description	Age
Silurian	mainly shales, mudstones, some limestones	417–443
Ordovician	mainly shales and limestones; limestone in Scotland	443–495
Cambrian	mainly shales and sandstones; limestone in Scotland	495–545
Late Precambrian	mainly sandstones, conglomerates and siltstones	545–1000

HIGHLY METAMORPHOSED ROCKS

Rock	Description	Age
Late Precambrian, Cambrian and Ordovician	mainly schists and gneisses	443–1000
Mid Precambrian	mainly gneisses	1500–3000

IGNEOUS ROCKS

Rock	Description
Intrusive	mainly granite, gabbro and dolerite
Volcanic	mainly basalt, rhyolite, andesite and volcanic ashes

Numbers indicate age in millions of years

Figure 5.7 (opposite) A simplified geological map of the British Isles. Sedimentary and metamorphic rocks are colour coded according to age. Igneous rocks are colour coded according to whether they are intrusive (i.e. crystallized below the Earth's surface) or volcanic (i.e. erupted at the Earth's surface, e.g. lava flows).

Even in areas where the bedrock is igneous or metamorphic, you will often be able to observe fossils in building stones, and in gravel used for paths and drives. Figure 5.8 shows several, rather worn, fossils found after an hour or so's searching in the gravel used around the Open University campus in Milton Keynes. Although the gravels were deposited by rivers in the Pleistocene, they are made up mainly of flint pieces derived from the Chalk, and they also contain numerous fragments of fossils, for example Jurassic oysters and belemnites. These fossils were mainly eroded out from their bedrock by ice and incorporated into glacial deposits before reworking by rivers later in the Pleistocene.

Figure 5.8 Fossils found in gravel used for paths and borders around the Open University campus in Milton Keynes. The largest specimen is 9 cm long. See if you can identify any before reading on. (Left column, top) Small fragment of a Pleistocene mammoth tooth (one of the many plates into which a tooth may split up; compare with tooth on top right of p.153 of the *Atlas*); (bottom) shell fragment of the Jurassic oyster *Gryphaea*, showing conspicuous growth lines. (Central column, top two) sponges from the Chalk preserved in association with flint; (third down) internal mould of part of the whorl of an ammonite showing impression of ribs; (bottom) worn fragment of a 'Devil's toenail', the Jurassic oyster *Gryphaea arcuata* (compare with Figure 4.4a). (Right column, top) fragment of flint internal mould of the Cretaceous echinoid *Echinocorys scutata* (compare with Figure 4.21a); (middle) scallop shell, probably Jurassic; (bottom) worn belemnite fragment, probably Jurassic.

Doing fieldwork

Safety is, of course, paramount. Here are some points relating to safety and conduct in the field; many are common sense.

- Always seek permission first if you intend to enter private land. Supervised, well-led, well-equipped parties may be allowed into working quarries, but individuals may be discouraged. Visitors to quarries have to wear hard hats (safety helmets), suitably tough footwear (e.g. walking boots) and high-visibility jackets. Keep away from machinery, deep water, sludge lagoons or wet areas that may be quicksand.
- On the coast, beware of tides, cliff falls and mudflows, especially during wet and stormy weather. The best time to collect is when the tide is going out.
- The cliffs on more rapidly eroding coastlines, and recently blasted quarry faces, are often exceedingly dangerous — never be tempted to go too close. A hard hat may give protection from a small pebble dislodged by a seagull, but is fatally useless against a more significant rockfall. Be careful, too, not to dislodge rock onto others below.
- Always wear safety goggles when hammering.
- Follow the Country Code, e.g. avoid disturbance of wildlife and do not leave the collecting site in an untidy or dangerous condition for those that follow.
- Even if you take a mobile phone, reception may be poor, so tell someone where you are going and what time you expect to return.

Many of the most important fossil sites in Britain are now protected by law as Sites of Special Scientific Interest (SSSIs) or designated as Regionally Important Geological Sites (RIGS) by local RIGS groups. They are also conserved by the nature conservation government agencies. For various reasons, collecting fossils or rocks from these sites may be prohibited, except for bona fide research purposes. In such cases special permission is required from the relevant countryside agency, i.e. the Countryside Council for Wales, English Nature or Scottish Natural Heritage. Where the fossil material is relatively common, responsible collecting is permitted. The key sites of Britain's geological heritage have been assessed by the Geological Conservation Review (GCR), initiated in 1977. Soon all the 2300 or so geological SSSIs will have been described comprehensively in a 42 volume series, details of which are available from the Joint Nature Conservation Committee (JNCC) in Peterborough.

Field equipment

Although a geological hammer is often useful, much study of fossils can be done without one. Indiscriminate hammering is a form of vandalism, and hammering is forbidden or even illegal at some sites. If there is a high risk of damaging a specimen when trying to extract it, then leave it for others to see or, if it is an important find, seek specialist help. An ordinary DIY hammer should not be used to break open any but the softest of rocks; the metal is too brittle, and metal chips may fly off. In any case, always protect your eyes with safety goggles. Geological hammers are made of specially hardened steel and come in various shapes.

A cold chisel (all metal) may be useful for prizing out pieces of rock and trimming matrix from specimens. A spade and sieve can sometimes be helpful in extracting fossils from soft clays or uncemented sands and silts. It is usually easier to remove the majority of matrix around the fossil in the field, rather than back at home, and there is less weight to carry too.

A notebook is essential, and annotated sketches, supplemented by photographs, are often the best way to record your observations. A long tape measure can help to record the precise position of important *in-situ* specimens. Even if you have no idea of a fossil's age, it is important to record the geographic location where you found it. Drawings and photos may, in fact, be a more desirable alternative to collecting, as the context in which fossils occur can be the main scientific interest.

You'll find your understanding of fossils and the rocks containing them greatly enhanced if you have a hand lens. These can be bought from stamp shops (philatelists) and some hobby shops. A magnification of ×10 is recommended.

You will need plastic bags, a non-smearing felt pen that will write in the rain, and some tissue paper (e.g. kitchen roll) to protect more delicate specimens.

The remains of Pleistocene vertebrates, such as mammoth teeth, tusks and other bones, once collected, must not be allowed to dry out, or they will usually split up into many pieces. Place them immediately in water or wet tissue until they can be treated. The splitting process can be effectively halted by immersing the fossil bone or tooth for 30 minutes in a moderately strong solution of PVA (polyvinyl acetate, easily purchased as a tin of wood glue) in water, draining it and leaving it to dry. Never varnish the surface of fossils — the surface becomes unnatural and the varnish eventually goes brown.

Cleaning, curating and identifying your specimens

Once you have made your finds, you will probably need to clean them. Unless the material is especially delicate (e.g. fossil fish scales or plant leaves), scrubbing under water with a soft brush may be all that's needed; use an old toothbrush for smaller fossils. Some specimens may need to have hard matrix removed. Ask your dentist for a few metal dental probes he or she would otherwise discard; these can readily be reground to a useful shape. For more stubborn matrix, an electric engraving tool may save a lot of effort. A museum should be able to give specialist advice on the safe use of dilute acids to remove limestone matrix.

Labelling where your finds come from is probably the single most important task: it is all too easy to forget the locality or remember it incorrectly. You will need to store your specimens, and will probably wish to display them: a wide variety of wooden or plastic sets of drawers, trays and shelves are available at larger DIY shops. It is a good idea to keep separately any fossils preserved in iron pyrites (fool's gold). Unfortunately, especially in humid conditions, this mineral can rot away, the fossil eventually crumbling to a pale crystalline powder which is acidic and corrodes paper and fabrics. It is not easy to tell which pyritized specimens will decay, and some are perfectly stable in ordinary conditions.

Fortunately, there are many books with fine illustrations to aid fossil identification and provide more information; some are listed in the *Atlas*, pp.216–217. Local museums are usually happy to offer advice and identify specimens found in the vicinity; they may also have a useful display. National museums (e.g. the Natural History Museum) usually offer an identification service, and their exhibits may allow you to identify some specimens for yourself. Only the best fossils in their collection are usually on display, so don't be discouraged if yours are not quite so impressive. For more problematic finds, large or specialized libraries hold palaeontological monographs and journals. Palaeontology is unusual in being one of the few branches of science where something written a century or more ago can be equally relevant today. The Internet is a marvellous source of information about fossils, evolution, etc: a few good websites are listed in the *Atlas*, p.203. Be aware, however, that the quality of information varies; the identification and provenance of fossils offered for sale, for example, may be highly inaccurate.

Although fossils may be viewed merely as attractive objects in their own right, their greatest value lies in the scientific information they can yield. If you think you've got a rare find, take your specimen, or send an image of it, to an expert. It is not uncommon for new species to be found by a complete beginner. The most important fossil finds may be far from spectacular in appearance. Once recognized as something significant, such as a new species, the specimen should be made available for an expert to describe and illustrate formally in a scientific paper. The specimen should be donated (or, exceptionally, sold) to an appropriate institution, usually a museum, where it can be curated, looked after in perpetuity and made accessible for others to study. Many a generous amateur collector has had a new species named after them.

Finally, there are many benefits in joining one of the numerous societies where you can meet others with a similar interest in fossils and rocks, discuss your finds and learn a great deal more. The local branch of the Open University Geological Society (OUGS), for example, would be an excellent start. The OUGS has over 3000 members in 18 regions, including mainland Europe, and arranges over 200 events in the UK and overseas each year, including field trips, lectures, and so on. You don't even have to be studying an OU course to join!

Comments on activities

Activity 3.1

Task 1

See Figure 3.29. The full name of this trilobite species, incidentally, is *Dalmanites myops*. You should now add the species name beside your drawing. Remember to underline these two words (Section 1.3). Note that another specimen of this species is shown on p.73 of the *Atlas*.

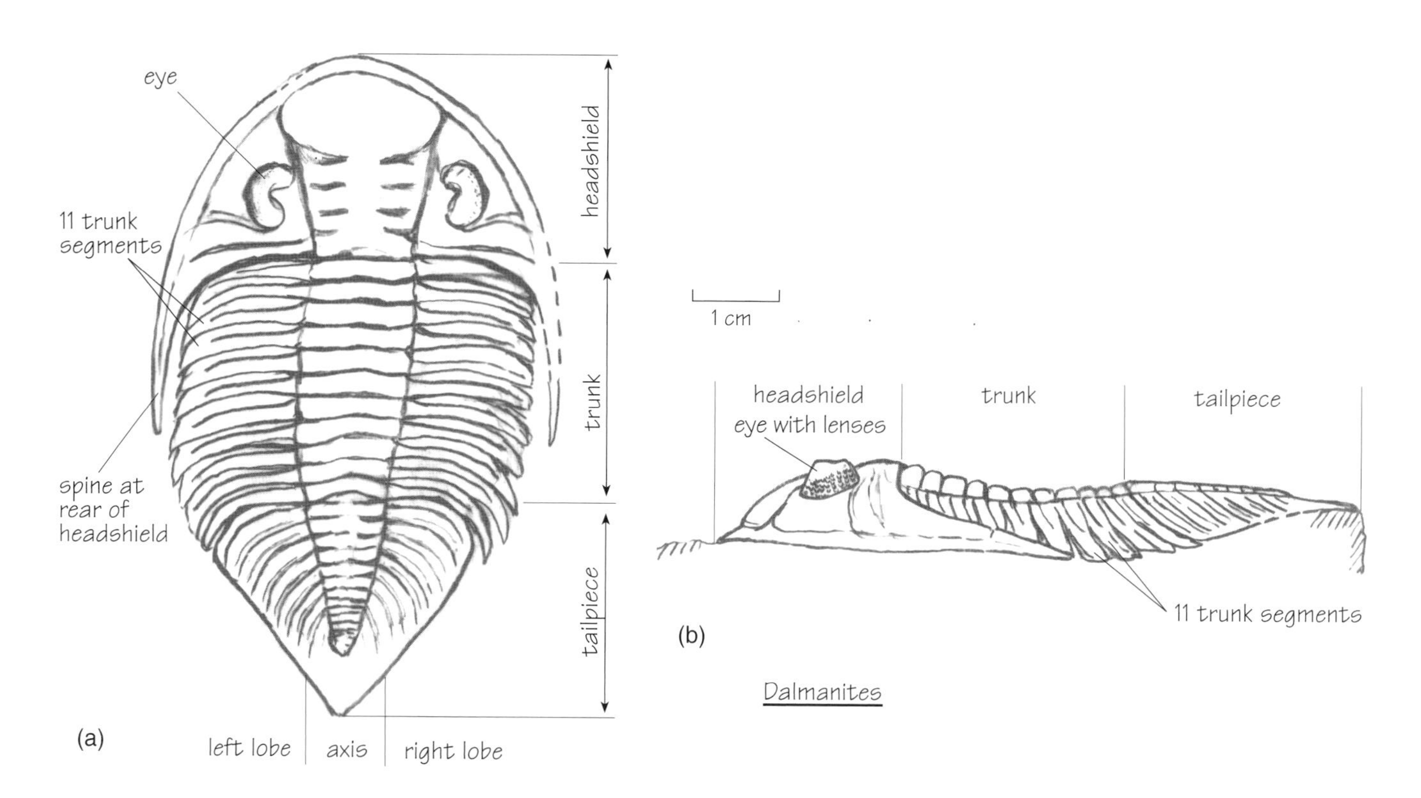

Figure 3.29 A completed Figure 3.4, for comparison with your own.

Task 2

See Figure 3.30. The full name of this crinoid species is *Marsupiocrinites coelatus*; you should now write this in, and underline the words.

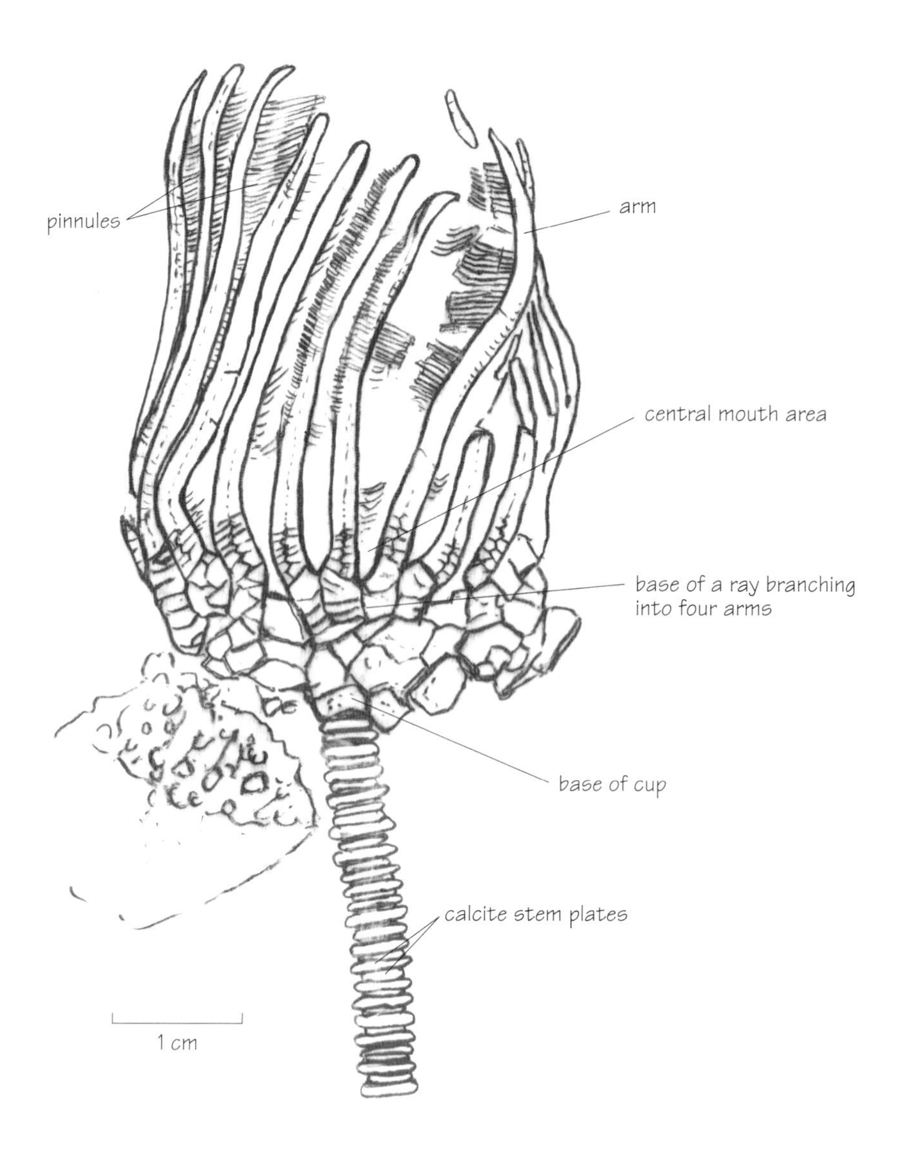

Figure 3.30 A completed Figure 3.9, for comparison with your own.

Activity 4.1

See Figure 4.29. For answers to Questions 4.2 and 4.3 see 'Questions: answers and comments'.

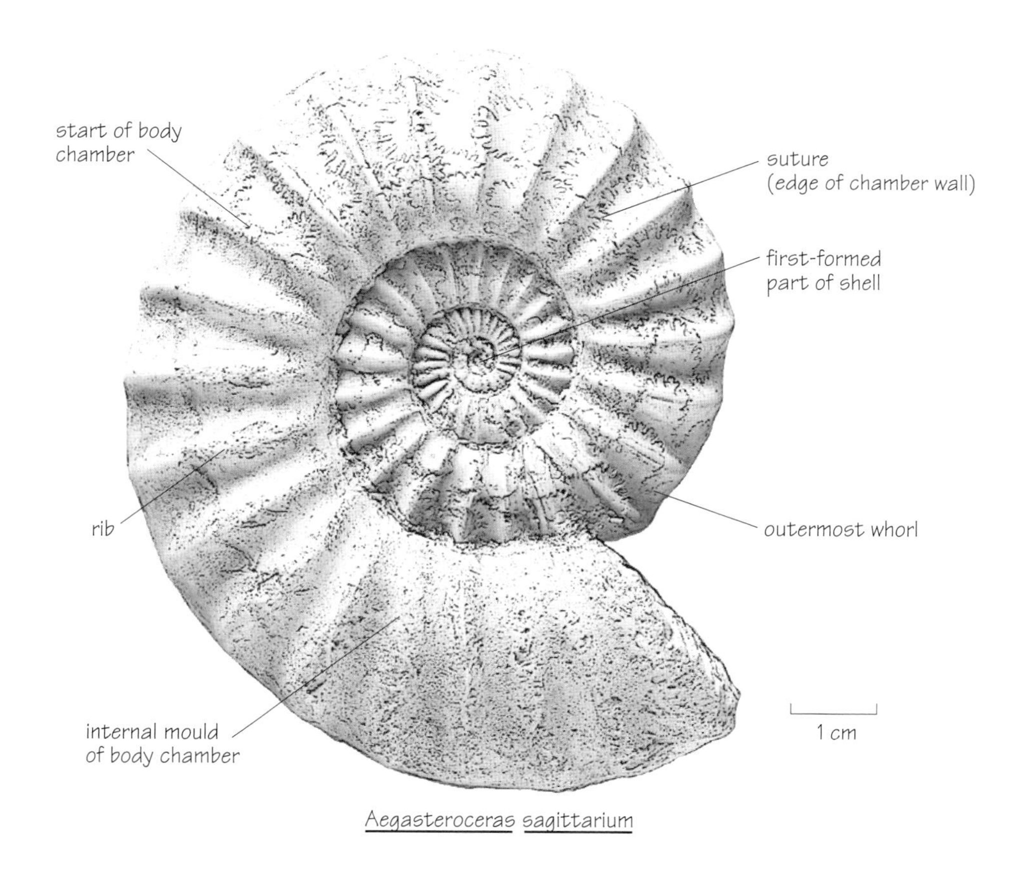

Figure 4.29 A labelled Figure 4.10, for comparison with your own.

Activity 4.2

See Figure 4.30.

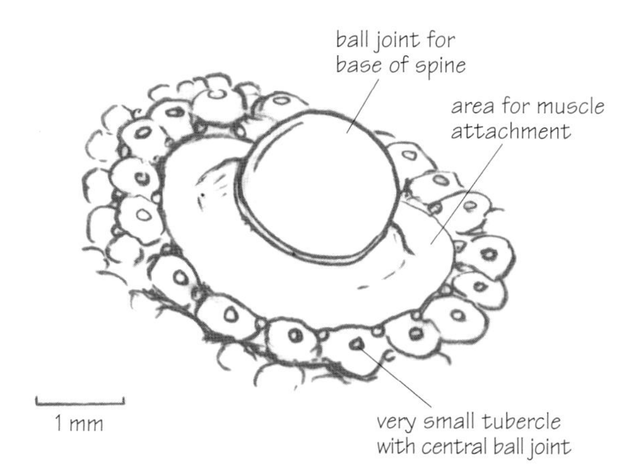

Figure 4.30 A completed Figure 4.20b, for comparison with your own.

Questions: answers and comments

Question 1.1 (a) The garden slug is extremely unlikely to find its way into the fossil record because it has only soft parts, and these will be eaten or will rapidly decay after death. In any case, living on land, it is in an environment with little chance of long-term burial by sediment. (b) The garden snail at least has a shell, but this too is readily destroyed, and overall the snail also has a low preservation potential because it lives on land. (c) The whale has huge bones, and being marine should stand a fair chance of fossilization. (d) The jellyfish, although living in the sea, has no hard parts, and, not surprisingly, fossil jellyfish are very rare.

Question 1.2 (a) As we saw in Question 1.1, any *individual* whale has, on average, a high preservation potential, but there are very few blue whales so the species is likely to be very rare in the fossil record. (b) The garden earthworm occurs in huge numbers, and is widespread, but, because it is soft-bodied and lives on land, both its body and its burrows are unlikely candidates for inclusion in the fossil record. (c) Despite having hard bones and teeth, the low numbers of individuals, the non-marine setting, and the fact that organic material on land in the tropics tends to be scavenged and to rot away very quickly, largely explain why early human fossils are so rare. (d) The oyster species is abundant, thick-shelled and marine, all of which give it by far the best preservation potential of these four species.

Question 1.3 (b), (c) and (e). (b) The trace fossils record its activities (though trace-makers are rarely preserved with their traces and so may be hard to identify); (c) the other groups could provide independent evidence of the environment; (e) the more complex the hard parts, the more clues to go on. Conversely, having few living relatives (a) tends to make fossils difficult to reconstruct as living organisms, and, (d), the more separated the hard parts, the more difficult to see where they fitted together, or whether they came from the same individual.

Question 1.4 (1) Precambrian; (2) 4600; (3) 545; (4) Phanerozoic; (5) 545; (6) older (*Atlas*, p.162); (7) dating; (8) superposition (*Atlas*, p.162); (9) unconformities (*Atlas*, p.163); (10) correlate; (11) Jurassic (*Atlas*, p.166) — they are also used for zoning Cretaceous rocks; (12) uncertainties.

Question 1.5 Fossils usually represent a small fraction of the total original organism. Normally only the hard parts are preserved, and these may be incomplete and merely isolated fragments (such as a single tooth). Living processes such as feeding, movement, behaviour, reproduction and interactions with other species cannot be directly observed and can only be inferred from the limited evidence retrievable from fossils. Reconstructions are particularly difficult for long-extinct groups with no close living relatives that can be used as models.

Question 3.1 The earliest generally recognized group of vertebrates to appear in the fossil record are fish, followed by amphibians, reptiles, mammals and finally birds.

Question 3.2 (a) It was a marine environment, because, on the basis of the information given, trilobites and crinoids (like other echinoderms, Section 1.4) are each known to have been entirely marine. (b) It was shallow enough for there to have been sufficient light for the trilobites to see by. As was stated earlier, most ancient crinoids lived in shallow water. Various other independent lines of evidence from the Wenlock Limestone suggest that the water was normally about 5–10 metres deep. (c) The water was probably clear most of the time, because, as was stated, muddy sediment can kill crinoids by clogging their feeding systems. (d) A sudden large influx of muddy sediment, completely burying the crinoid and/or clogging its feeding system, may have been responsible for its death. (In fact, the original specimen shows that the crinoid lies within a layer of mud, supporting this suggestion.) Such sediment influxes, usually during major storms, are known today to kill off some types of organism, and the trilobite may have met its demise in a similar way. (e) The dead individuals cannot have been exposed for long after death to persistent, strong currents because the trilobite skeleton is in one piece and the crinoid plates have also remained very largely intact. This interpretation is consistent with the suggestion that a thick layer of muddy sediment covered the animals (either at, or shortly after, death), protecting the bodies from disruption by currents.

Question 3.3 There are approximately 40 families of living reptiles. So the average number of species per family is 6500 divided by 40 $\approx$163. There are about 150 families of living mammals and 4300 species, giving an average of 4300 divided by 150 $\approx$29. Thus living reptiles have far more species per family than mammals.

Question 3.4 The approximate numbers of end Permian families are: sharks and rays (20), bony fishes (25), amphibians (35) and reptiles (20) — total 100. Early Triassic families: sharks and rays (10), bony fishes (10), amphibians (10) and reptiles (5) — total 35. There was therefore a 65% decrease in family diversity across the Permian–Triassic boundary.

Question 3.5 Many people could not reconcile the idea of extinction with the religious view of a natural world planned and made perfect by God. (See also the *Atlas*, p.102.)

Question 3.6 (a) Georges Cuvier; (b) Charles Lyell. Further biographical information is given in the *Atlas*, p.198 (Cuvier) and p.200 (Lyell).

Question 3.7 There are always some environmental changes taking place, and the way that the various Earth systems are linked together is immensely complex. The evidence during mass extinctions often points to several environmental factors acting together. However, merely showing that certain events were correlated in time during extinctions is very different from establishing the full chain of cause and effect: as the programme demonstrates, establishing this is very difficult, even for more recent extinctions such as that of the mammoth.

Question 3.8 It is likely that climate change or human hunting or, quite probably, a combination of both, were responsible for the extinction of mammoths. It is, however, impossible to ascertain which of these two factors was more important. About 15 000 to 10 000 years ago, climate change (global warming) caused a change in vegetation and, at the same time, hunting increased as, for example, when North America was colonized by humans. Modelling shows that only a small increase in the percentage of mammoths killed by humans could have rapidly led to a terminal decline in mammoth populations.

Question 4.1 1: Placodonts: shellfish; 2: nothosaurs: fish; 3: ichthyosaurs (*Atlas G*, p.210): fish and belemnites; 4: plesiosaurs (*Atlas G*, p.213): fish; 5: pliosaurs (short-necked plesiosaurs): fish, ichthyosaurs and smaller plesiosaurs. The diet is revealed by stomach contents and coprolites (fossilized droppings) (*Atlas*, p.97). The shape of the teeth may also be a strong clue.

Question 4.2 (a) The sutures are about 8.5 mm apart. (b) The ribs are about 11 mm apart. Note that it is important to specify where such measurements are taken because the distance separating sutures and ribs decreases towards the centre of the ammonite.

Question 4.3 About 24 mm. You need to double up the half-width (about 12 mm) at the end of the body chamber.

Question 4.4 The pattern in both periods is, in general, very similar, as in each case sea level starts relatively low, after a fall at the end of the previous period, and then fairly steadily increases before decreasing again at the end. Sea level at the end of the Cretaceous was very similar to that at the start. The average sea level in the Cretaceous was higher than that in the Jurassic.

Question 4.5 (a) *Oviraptor* was found sitting on its own nest; the eggs turned out to contain *Oviraptor* embryos, not those of *Protoceratops* (*Atlas*, p.116). (b) In late Cretaceous times, the most abundant mammals were the multituberculates, which probably ate plants (*Atlas*, p.117). (c) *Tyrannosaurus rex* has been estimated to have had a maximum speed of only 19 miles (30 km) per hour. It may have been mainly a scavenger rather than an active predator (*Atlas*, p.119).

Question 4.6 The mosasaurs evolved from a group of *land-living lizards* in the *mid-Cretaceous* (*Atlas G*, p.211). They were mainly propelled through the water by their *tail*. After thriving for *25* million years, they became extinct *65* million years ago (*Atlas*, p.121), and their niche in the world's oceans was soon taken up by *marine mammals* in the early Cenozoic Era (*Atlas*, p.121). (Ichthyosaurs had died out earlier in the Cretaceous.)

Question 4.7 1: charcoal. 2: wildfires. 3: fall. 4: global warming. 5: acid rain (sulphuric acid in this case). 6: southern. 7: 75%. 8: America. 9: flowering plants (angiosperms). 10: ferns. For 1, 2, 3 and 5, see the *Atlas*, p.127. For 4 see above (Section 4.11) and for 6–10 see the *Atlas*, p.129.

Question 4.8 (a) There *is* evidence that dinosaurs were in decline before the K–T impact. Some predatory theropod groups (e.g. the ostrich-like ornithomimids) declined in numbers and diversity during the last few million years before the meteorite struck (*Atlas*, p.125). (b) The only thing wrong here is that the head-butting pachycephalosaurid is *Stegoceras*, not *Stegosaurus*. *Stegosaurus* is a Jurassic genus (*Atlas*, p.99), and although there were late Cretaceous stegosaurs, the group became extinct before the end of the Cretaceous (Figure 4.2). (c) *Quetzalcoatlus* was a pterosaur, not a dinosaur (*Atlas*, p.124); there were no flying dinosaurs.

Question 5.1 (a) These groups moved from South America into North America (*Atlas*, pp.148–149). (b) Glyptodonts were *placental* mammals (*Atlas*, p.148). (c) *Hyracotherium* was about the size of a *labrador dog* (*Atlas*, p.149). (d) The levels of extinction in the two continents were *similar* and the total mammal population *increased* in South America (*Atlas*, p.149).

Question 5.2 The fundamental problem is the very poor preservation potential of hominids, as we saw in Question 1.2 (c). Compared with marine invertebrates, the number of individual vertebrates tend to be far fewer. Organic material on land in the tropics tends to be scavenged and to rot away very quickly. Even if bones and teeth are incorporated into sediment, most non-marine deposits are in the process of being removed by erosion: only certain conditions on land allow major accumulations of sediment, such as subsiding lake basins and structural depressions such as rift valleys (*Atlas G*, p.213).

Question 5.3 Check that all the following correct answers are eventually written in to provide the completed summary. References are to pages in the *Atlas* unless otherwise indicated. 1: pygmy chimp (p.150); 2: 28 (p.150); 3: australopithecines (p.150); 4: *ramidus* (p.151); 5: *afarensis* (p.145); 6: 2.5 (p.145); 7: *Homo* (p.145); 8: *habilis* (p.146, 156); 9: *erectus* (pp.146, 156); 10: 1.75 (p.146); 11: 1.8 (p.156); 12: Acheulian (p.146); 13: *sapiens* (pp.145, 157); 14: 40 000 (p.157); 15: *neanderthalensis* (p.156); 16: 30 000 (p.156); 17: 365 000 (p.157); 18: *heidelbergensis* (Figure 5.2); 19: *antecessor* (Figure 5.2); 20: Cro-Magnons (p.157); 21: Bering land bridge (p.157); 22: Ice Age (p.157); 23: 30 000 (p.157); 24: Clovis (p.157).

Question 5.4 Assuming life on Earth began about 4000 Ma ago (Section 2), then the calculation is as follows: $200\,000/4000\,000\,000 \times 100\% = 0.005\%$, i.e. five thousandths of 1%.

Question 5.5 (a) Incorrect: the Quaternary Ice Age is only the most recent of many ice ages (*Atlas*, p.152). The next most recent one occurred during the late Carboniferous and early Permian (*Atlas*, p.80). (b) Correct: see *Atlas*, pp.152, 159. (c) Incorrect: lowering of sea level due to glaciation meant that parts of what is now the North Sea became dry land on which mammoths were able to live (*Atlas*, p.159). (d) Incorrect: sea levels fell by about 100 m (*Atlas*, p.152) or perhaps as much as 120 m. (e) Correct: see *Atlas*, p.153. (f) Correct: see *Atlas*, pp.158–159.

Acknowledgements

Grateful acknowledgement is made to the following sources for permission to reproduce material in this book.

Figures

Figure 1.1a: J. Chester Farnsworth, Princeton University Natural History Museum; *Figure 1.1b*: courtesy of Martin Lockley; *Figures 1.2, 1.6, 1.8, 1.9, 1.13, 3.1, 3.2, 3.4, 3.6–3.13, 3.28–3.30, 4.3, 4.4, 4.6–4.10, 4.12–4.17, 4.20–4.27a, 4.30, 5.5, 5.6a and 5.8*: Peter Sheldon; *Figure 1.3*: courtesy of Nick P. Branch; *Figure 1.4*: photograph by Frank M. Carpenter; *Figure 1.5*: courtesy of Andrew Scott; *Figures 1.10a and 1.12a*: Heather Angel; *Figures 1.10b and 4.11*: Clarkson, E. N. K. (1998) *Invertebrate Palaeontology and Evolution*, fourth edition, Blackwell Science; *Figures 1.11 and 1.12b*: Fish, J. D. and Fish, S. (1989) *A Student's Guide to the Seashore*, Unwin Hyman, Chapman and Hall, Inc.; *Figure 2.1*: courtesy of J. W. Schopf; *Figure 2.2*: courtesy of Nick Butterfield; *Figure 3.3a*: National Museum of Wales; *Figure 3.3b*: courtesy of Jason Dunlop; *Figure 3.14, 4.1 and 4.2*: adapted from Benton, M. J. (2000) *Vertebrate Palaeontology*, second edition, Blackwell Science; *Figures 3.16–3.27, 4.18*: Bob Spicer; *Figure 4.5*: courtesy of P. Laboute/Jacana; *Figure 4.27b*: courtesy of Bruce F. Bohor; *Figure 4.28a*: courtesy of Jeremy Young; *Figure 4.28b*: courtesy of Kate Harcourt-Brown; *Figure 5.1:* Stanley, S. M. (1993) *Exploring Earth and Life Through Time*, p.409, copyright © W. H. Freeman & Company; *Figure 5.2*: compiled by Douglas Palmer; *Figure 5.3:* Copyright © The Natural History Museum; *Figure 5.4*: courtesy of Adrian Lister; *Figure 5.6b*: courtesy of Mike Barker; *Figure 5.7:* reproduced by permission of the British Geological Survey © NERC. All rights reserved.

Title page

John Watson

Every effort has been made to trace all copyright owners, but if any has been inadvertently overlooked, the publishers will be pleased to make the necessary arrangements at the first opportunity.

Index

Note that section summaries are not included in this index.